PROCESS PLANT COMMISSIONING – A USER GUIDE

D.M.C. Horsley and J.S. Parkinson (Editors)

INSTITUTION OF CHEMICAL ENGINEERS

The information in this Guide is given in good
faith and belief in its accuracy, but does not
imply the acceptance of any legal liability or
responsibility whatsoever, by the Institution, the
Editors or by individual members of the
Working Party for the consequences of its use
or misuse in any particular circumstances.

Published by
Institution of Chemical Engineers
Davis Building
165-171 Railway Terrace
Rugby, Warwickshire, CV21 3HQ, England

Copyright © 1990
Institution of Chemical Engineers

ISBN 0 85295 260 0

Printed by The Chameleon Press Limited, 5–25 Burr Road, London SW18 4SG

FOREWORD

The Institution's Engineering Practice Committee is to be warmly congratulated on initiating a user guide on "Process Plant Commissioning", and on identifying a very strong team to execute the project in exemplary fashion. The guide they have produced is rich in valuable perceptions based on much distilled wisdom and experience, in addition to providing a systematic and complete treatment of the subject.

By the time the commissioning stage is reached, major capital will have been spent, and the corporate climate is likely to be one of high expectancy, some anxiety and a degree of impatience. The project will have been undertaken in the expectation of meeting a market need, often with a great deal of urgency.

This adds to the psychological burden of what is in any event the climax of a substantial multi-disciplinary engineering effort led by the process engineering discipline, not infrequently preceded and supported by considerable research investment.

Looking back on a career rich in commissioning experience I have no doubt that, of all the project stages, the commissioning phase is the most demanding in skill, judgement, leadership, perseverance, courage and sheer physical endurance. It also has abnormal potential for hazard.

Whereas there will be wide variations in scale and complexity, in contractual arrangements and in the degree of process innovation, commissioning imposes a specific approach to the management of the four interlocking elements involved:

- The Commissioning Team;
- The Plant;
- The Process;
- Raw Materials, Intermediates, Products.

The additional dimensions required in each case, compared with normal operation, emerge from the guide with great clarity.

It is equally explicit on the main ingredients of success:

- Meticulous attention to Safety and Hazards;
- An ably led, well balanced, well trained and committed commissioning team, capable of absorbing the physical and psychological stress;
- Adequate involvement in the design phase and safety studies;
- Thorough planning, implementation and control of commissioning preparations;
- Ready availability of help from supporting disciplines to deal with specific problems identified;
- An expeditious approval system for agreeing plant modifications;
- A well structured relationship at senior level with site construction management, and with future operational management.

I applaud the reference to the "Post Commissioning Phase". The proper recording of modifications is a vital task, as is the preservation of performance tests as datum points for continuing operation. Of even greater long term significance is a detailed post-commissioning review, recording all that has been done to improve the reliability and operability of the plant during the commissioning phase. It should moreover capitalise on the deep insights gained, by defining targets for further performance improvement and cost reduction.

The work is enhanced by a most useful set of Appendices, providing a great variety of checklists including, *inter alia*, final checks before introducing process materials, safety assessment of modifications, equipment check out by categories, piping systems, electrics, control systems and storage.

This guide makes available to the profession much hard won and valuable experience for which we are greatly indebted to the members of the Working Party, and their employing organisations. It will make a major contribution to safer and more efficient commissioning of process plants in the years ahead, and to the professional development of Process Engineers.

R.J. Kingsley

MEMBERSHIP OF THE WORKING PARTY

MEMBERS

J.S. Parkinson (Chairman)	Courtaulds Research
J. Broughton	Babcock Robey Ltd
D.M.C. Horsley	British Nuclear Fuels plc
J. Love	University of Leeds
F.J. Owen	Harcros Chemicals UK Ltd
L. Pearson	ICI (retired)
R.B.S. Prior	H&G Engineering (retired)
N.F. Scilly	Health & Safety Executive
P. Snowdon	University of Leeds
L.F. Stooks	APV Baker Ltd

CORRESPONDING MEMBERS

M.H.J. Ashley	John Brown Engineers & Constructors Ltd
J.B. Brennard	Consultant
K. Griffiths	Leigh Group
J. Lindley	ICI

ACKNOWLEDGEMENTS

The support and encouragement given to members of the Working Party by their respective employing organisations is gratefully acknowledged. In addition the Working Party wishes to record its thanks to several members of the Institution who have provided detailed and constructive comment on the draft text.

Responsibility for the contents remains with the authors and the editors.

Extracts from BS 6739:1986 are reproduced with the permission of BSI. Complete copies can be obtained by post from BSI Sales, Linford Wood, Milton Keynes, MK14 6LE; telex 825777 BSIMK G; telefax 0908 320856.

CONTENTS

CONTENTS

1.   INTRODUCTION

This guide provides information on the commissioning of process plant. The guide does not restrict itself to chemical plant and is intended to be equally useful to those employed in the food and allied industries. Likewise the guide should be useful for the commissioning of small plant as well as large plant. Although most of the guide deals with the commissioning of plant in the UK, a section addresses some of the problems of commissioning plant overseas.

The aim has been to provide a document which gives the non-specialist engineer advice on how to set about the problem of commissioning either a new plant or indeed a modification to an existing plant. Some aspects of decommissioning process plant have also been included.

Careful consideration has been given to the layout of this guide. It is suggested that users start at the beginning and work through the text, although for those needing only a "refresher" some useful check-lists have been provided in the Appendices.

In addition, a glossary of terms is included. In this a definition of "specialist" terminology is provided.

Commissioning of process plant is most commonly the responsibility of one of the following:
• the owner, if, for example, the project is managed and executed "in-house" by an Operating Company utilising perhaps its own process technology.
• a contractor, if responsibility for the project or for some aspects of it has been "let" by the owner. In such cases the process package may be proprietary to the owner, contractor, or to the licensor, or to a combination of these.

Whichever case applies, the commissioning operation requires meticulous attention both in the preparation of stages and in subsequent execution. This guide seeks to identify and highlight the more important features to be considered in all phases of commissioning.

A block diagram showing the phases of a typical project and the place of the commissioning activities described in this guide is shown in Figure 1.1.

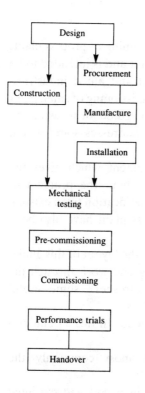

Figure 1.1   Typical phases of a project

2. CONTRACTS, PLANNING AND ADMINISTRATION

1. TYPES OF CONTRACT

The importance of contract form needs to be appreciated whether a project is predominantly "in-house" with perhaps relatively small involvement of sub-contractors, or the entire work is to be entrusted to a Contractor. Responsibility for commissioning needs to be clearly defined if ambiguities at a later stage are to be avoided.

A wide range of types of contract exist. These cover all likely combinations from "turn-key" to fully reimbursable contracts. At the enquiry or bid stage of the project the definitions of responsibility must be carefully considered together with the General Conditions of Contract.

There are a number of model Conditions of Contract for process plants, amongst them those published by the Institution of Chemical Engineers for lump-sum and reimbursable contracts respectively (Reference 1, Reference 2). They provide well-defined guidelines concerning related responsibilities, terminology and documentation appropriate to all stages of a contract, including commissioning. Whilst designed for work in the UK, they may also be used as a basis for preparation of Conditions of Contract for work in other countries.

If a recognized model form of Conditions of Contract is not to be used, it is nonetheless important that the Contract should define the split of work and responsibility between client and contractor. Table 2.1 contains extracts from a procedure developed by one UK process plant contractor to define such responsibilities. At the same time it identifies activities which interface between construction and commissioning. Procedures of this type may need to be adapted to suit the type and complexity of a particular plant.

Whatever form of Conditions of Contract is to be used it is important that the requirements for completion of respective phases of the contract are clearly defined. Such milestones in the progress of site

3

Table 2.1
Defining work and responsibility of construction and commissioning by contractor and the client*

Construction and
PreCommissioning:

PHASE A Prepare plant/equipment for pre-commissioning/mechanical testing
PHASE B Prepare services; clean and pressure test systems
PHASE C Check and prepare major mechanical equipment, instrumentation, and protection systems
PHASE D Final preparations for start-up

Commissioning:

PHASE E Charge with feedstock, etc. Start-up plant and operate
PHASE F Performance test and plant acceptance
PHASE G Remainder of Maintenance Period

	PHASE	A	B	C	D	E	F	G
1	Control of works by:		Contractor Construction				Client	
2	Basic responsibilities and phases for various categories of staff at site							
	Construction		Site Manager and team of Construction Specialists			Defects correction under contractor's direction		Return for corrective work
	Contractor Comm		Witnessing Inspection & Testing			Advising start-up & operation of plant	Wit-nessing Perform. Test	
				Training Client's Operators				
	Client		Witnessing Inspection & Testing			Plant maintenance and normal adjustments by Client		
				Operators receiving training		Preparing for start-up; starting-up and operating plant.		
	Equipment Vendors		Testing and commissioning presence on site			On call to site to end of maintenance period		
3	On completion of construction		CERTIFICATE OF MECHANICAL COMPLETION/TAKING OVER CERTIFICATE			CERTIFICATE OF ACCEPTANCE OF PLANT PERFORMANCE		
								FINAL CERTIFICATE

* See Appendix 2 for schedules listing principle work carried out in respective phases and by whom.

activities are usually formalized by appropriate certification. To these may be linked stage-payments, or transfer of ownership with its significant effect on insurance liabilities.

Terminology relating to phase completion at site requires to be specific particularly in respect of pre-commissioning. Pre-commissioning usually commences during the latter stages of construction with which it has to be carefully integrated. 'Completion of erection' or 'mechanical completion' are two terms commonly used in model Conditions of Contract and frequently relate to readiness of the plant (or part of), to be commissioned using process feedstocks, or otherwise made 'live'. Thus all pre-commissioning is included by definition. In some instances this may not be so, stipulated mechanical tests having to be fulfilled before the completion of erection certificate may be submitted; pre-commissioning then follows.

2.   QUALITY ASSURANCE

Engineering of process plant projects increasingly involves the application of a disciplined management system which will ensure that the quality of product or service is built in at every stage. In this context quality is defined as "fitness for purpose", that is, the product must be fit for the purpose for which it is designed.

It is important to establish at the outset of a project whether Quality Assurance is to be applied. Quality Assurance requirements are directly applicable to four key areas:
- the design and specification of the plant;
- supply of equipment and services to the design specification by the contractor and all sub-contractors;
- erection, installation and testing of the equipment to the design specification by the contractor and all sub-contractors;
- operation of the completed plant to achieve design performance consistently.

Clearly the first three areas relate to assuring the quality of the plant which is being built. Use at every stage of companies which have a proven Quality Assurance System and which may well be registered with an accredited scheme (such as that of British Standards Institution BS 5750/ISO 9000) will assure a high level of workmanship and minimize rectification work. (Reference 3 and Reference 5).

The application of Quality Assurance to pre-commissioning

commencing, preferably, with early involvement in the design phase, will prove beneficial and minimize problems that affect pre-commissioning. The same structured approach should then be applied to testing programmes at equipment vendor's factories, through to site construction, pre-commissioning and functional testing phases.

The fourth area listed above relates to how the plant is designed, controlled and operated to achieve consistent performance and the necessary corrective action to be taken when it fails to do this. At all stages of commissioning two questions need to be asked when changes are proposed:

• "What effect, if any, does this action have on the ability of the plant to perform consistently within design specification?" (Any change must be referred back to the design authority and correctly logged).

• "Does the change comply with the appropriate Quality Manual?"

3. COMMISSIONING ESTIMATES

A manpower cost estimate for commissioning staff is a usual element of the overall project costing for tender or budget purposes. It must take full account of all disciplines involved in commissioning, the hours including overtime that they may work, the back up services that they will need and the site allowances, travel and accommodation costs which they will be paid. Previous experience of similar plants is valuable for this purpose. Such information may be available as a computerized data base.

It may be necessary to separate pre-commissioning costs from those for commissioning. This will be so if pre-commissioning is to be included in a firm or fixed price estimate and the commissioning is reimbursable. This sometimes occurs, especially if the ultimate owner's process technology is involved.

It is most important when putting together the budget for a project to make adequate allowance (either as a specific allocation or within contingency) to cover the cost of modifications which will inevitably be required during or as a result of commissioning tests.

RESOURCING

The manpower estimate will need to take account of whether all resources are available in-house or whether it is expected to hire-in supplementary personnel. When deciding upon the manning strategy for a project it may be necessary to consider all other company demands upon resources over the project timescale. Cost-effectiveness of available alternatives will need to be taken into account.

A further factor to be considered is the possibly disruptive effect of imbalance between permanent and hired staff, although this is more directly relevant when actually selecting a commissioning team.

When a Quality Assurance System is included provision for the greater involvement of commissioning personnel with all disciplines at a relatively early stage of the project will need to be taken into account. Such provision will also need to include preparation of detailed procedures and generation of associated documentation.

PROGRAMMING

Project programmes generally need to include specific reference to the pre-commissioning, commissioning and performance testing phases. These must be aligned with definitions appropriate to the particular Conditions of Contract referred to earlier.

PERSONNEL ASPECTS

Costs relating to aspects such as inducements, status, travel, accommodation and living allowances, must be considered, particularly in respect of overseas projects.

Inducements may need to take account of Conditions of Employment of the personnel likely to be involved, especially if field assignments such as commissioning constitute a departure from the norm and hence involve disturbance factors.

CRAFTS INVOLVEMENT

The construction element is not included in this Guide except in relation to specific requirements for pre-commissioning and commissioning. The need for adequate numbers of supervisory and crafts personnel should not be overlooked.

Construction estimates will usually take into account requirements up to completion of erection and these should include a small team of respective crafts disciplines with supervisors to work under the general direction of commissioning staff responsible for pre-commissioning. If such responsibility extends into the commissioning phase it is prudent to make allowance for continuing involvement to cover remedial or rectification work as well as commissioning adjustments. Usually a small team is required on shift (or at least available on call out) during start-up and initial operation of the plant.

Instrumentation usually requires the involvement of a significant number of technicians in all of the above phases and on shift during start-up. It is sometimes necessary to differentiate between instrument fitters and instrument technicians. Instrument technicians' particular skills are in calibration, setting-up, loop-checking and optimizing settings on the installed equipment.

4.   THE PROJECT STAGE – EARLY PREPARATIONS

The first activities to involve commissioning personnel are likely to include:

- preparation of training programmes, where necessary;
- involvement in the design phase;
- check listing of engineering and utilities line diagrams, (ELD's and ULD's);
- preparation of equipment check-out schedules;
- planning of pre-commissioning and commissioning activities for inclusion in the project and construction programmes.

TRAINING

Responsibility for training 'key' members of the eventual operating and maintenance teams often rests with commissioning personnel under the direction of the project manager and in liaison with respective engineering disciplines (see Chapter 4). The extent of the contractor's responsibilities for training the client's operators and/or technicians must be clearly defined in the Conditions of Contract.

INVOLVEMENT IN DESIGN PHASE

Involvement in the design facilitates the inclusion of advantageous features and designing out of problems that affect pre-commissioning, start-up and operation of the plant.

PREPARATION OF CHECK LISTS

Commissioning staff may participate effectively in a review of line diagrams using check lists prepared using information from experience

8

of similar plants or equipment. This type of check corresponds in part to HAZOP checks generally practised for new projects.

An effective retrieval system for experience gained in respect of similar plants or situations can be very helpful when reviewing procedures/designs for new projects and in resolving problems during commissioning (see Chapter 9, Section 4 "Audits/Reviews").

EQUIPMENT CHECK OUT SCHEDULES

An audited Quality Assurance System should include a suitably structured approach to safe pre-commissioning and commissioning operations.

Check sheets, or schedules, appropriate to the particular phase and activity should be available, commencing with those required during testing at the equipment vendor's factory, through to construction and pre-commissioning. (See Chapter 5.)

The check sheets may be pre-printed with standard questions annotated against process and engineering data sheets and vendor's drawings. They are signed off by respective authorities after individual checks have been witnessed and will eventually form part of the project handover documentation.

Examples of check sheets developed by one UK process plant contractor are included in Appendix 2.1 to 2.5.

Any procedures relating to specific activities of pre-commissioning and commissioning must be available with the check sheets.

Statutory requirements will usually reinforce the need for proper completion of all verification documentation before a plant can be put into operation. The Commissioning Manager must resist pressures to take short cuts in the supposed interest of expediting start-up.

ACTIVITY PLANNING

The importance of careful, detailed planning of all phases of testing and commissioning cannot be over-emphasized.

Commissioning needs to be considered in good time within the overall project programme. Pre-commissioning activities have to be integrated into the construction programme to provide the best logical sequence for start-up preparations. Assessments must be made of when

Line	Task No.	Category	Activity Description	1	2	3	4	5	6
1		Process							
2	12	"	Check out/line flush and pre. comm. equip. in crude unit area						
3	13	"	Check out/line flush and pre. comm. equip. in hydrotreat area						
4	14	"	Check out/line flush and pre. comm. equip. in reformer area						
5	15	"	Check out/line flush adn pre. comm. equip. in LPG unit area						
6	16	"	Flush fuel gas/fuel oil main						
7	17	"	Check out/line flush flare system						
8	18	"	Pressure test fuel gas/fuel oil main						
9	19	"	Pressure test flare system						
10	20	"	Load de-ethaniser column						
11	21	"	Load hydrotreater reactor						
12	28	"	Dry crude heater refractory						
13	29	"	Dry heaters – hydrotreater unit						
14	30	"	Chemical clean – compressor pipework						
15	31	"	Pre-commission and run in compressors						
16	32	"	Pressure test crude unit						
17	33	"	Pressure test hydrotreater						
18	34	"	Pressure test reformer unit						
19	35	"	Pressure test LPG unit						
20	39	"	Circulate crude oil in crude unit						
21	40	"	Heat crude furnace and commence tower circulation						
22	42	"	Commission desalter						
23	43	"	Commission stabilisor/fractionator on hydrotreater						
24	44	"	Excess fuel/LPG to flare						
25	45	"	N2 circulation on reformer						
26	46	"	Dry reformer reactors and refractory on fired heaters						
27	47	"	Charge catalyst to reformer						
28	48	"	Final pressure test reformer/purge with N2 and then H2						
29	49	"	Produce acceptable feed for reformer start up						
30	51	"	Circulate with H2 and heat reformer reactors						
31	52	"	Commission stabiliser on reformer unit						
32	53	"	Condition reformer catalyst						
33	54	"	Introduce feed to reformer						
34	55	"	Circulate N2 on hydrotreater reactor and heat						
35	56	"	Introduce hydrogen and feed to hydrotreater reactor						
36	57	"	Produce on spec. products from hydrotreater area						
37	58	"	Commission caustic and water wash vessels in LPG area						
38	59	"	Commission feed to LPG unit						
39	63	"	Trim units/conduct performance tests						
40									

Figure 2.1 Typical commissioning planning bar chart (part of).

Week No.

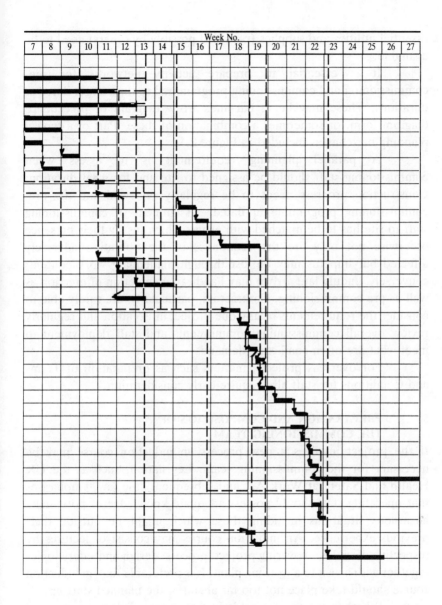

essential utilities and supplies (provided possibly by others) need to be available.

It is essential to prepare activity networks for pre-commissioning and commissioning programmed against target dates or durations. These may be in bar-line, arrow diagram or precedence diagram form, or sometimes a combination of these. Part of a typical planning bar-chart is included as Figure 2.1.

A parallel planning requirement is to assess when commissioning staff should be assigned to site and for what duration. Construction progress needs to be regularly reviewed and the pre-commissioning programme up-dated. Assignment of commissioning staff to site has to be matched with events which justify their presence otherwise not only are the economics of the operation adversely affected but impetus may be lost through inadequate work content; conversely, unduly late arrival may handicap completion of erection as well as pre-commissioning. Contractors, particularly, are rarely able to consider the requirements of any one project in isolation and regularly review overall commissioning commitments and staff deployment to meet what are often conflicting demands.

For overseas projects, matters such as preparation of Terms and Conditions for staff also require early consideration.

5.   PREPARATION AND COMPOSITION OF THE COMMISSIONING TEAM

If the project involves a new process an induction course may be necessary for the commissioning team. Legislation, such as the UK Health and Safety at Work Act and subsequent case law, emphasises that operating staff should possess adequate knowledge of potentially hazardous situations including those which might be outside their previous experience. An induction course may consist of lectures by respective disciplines covering project, process, design and safety topics together with a visit to a working plant. It is preferable that an induction course should take place not too far ahead of the planned start-up.

Whether or not a formal induction is arranged, it is customary for members of the commissioning team to attend a briefing before proceeding to site. For the Commissioning Manager this may involve an extended period during which he will become familiar with the background of the project.

Ideally the commissioning team should consist of engineers with relevant experience who have previously worked together. It is important to ensure that within the team there is sufficient depth of experience in all aspects of plant pre-commissioning and commissioning. A successful team may well include a balance between those of theoretical and practical ability.

Whilst technical competence has to be carefully considered when selecting the commissioning team, personality aspects are no less important. Choice of the Commissioning Manager must give consideration to his abilities as a team leader; compatibility of team members has similarly to be taken into account relative to the conditions of physical and psychological stress often experienced during plant start-up. Such demands may be particularly severe when the site is a foreign location.

The size of the commissioning team may vary with the type and complexity of the installation as well as with the contractual requirements and experience of the operating personnel. As an example, the typical composition of a contractor's commissioning team on a large ammonia plant might be:
- Commissioning Manager and Deputy;
- 4 Shift Leaders;
- 4 Assistants;
- Instrument, Mechanical and Electrical Specialists;
- Chemist.

It is preferable to provide for a 4-shift rota to avoid extended working hours. Critical start-up operations may necessitate a doubling-up of personnel to provide 12-hour shift cover for a period.

6.   ON-SITE ACTIVITIES

For the large ammonia plant referred to in the previous section, it would be normal to have contractor's commissioning staff at site at least 4 months prior to start-up. A progressive build-up of the team would occur during this period. The stage at which continuous attendance of commissioning staff is required at site varies with the type and size of installation as well as contractual conditions; as does the rate of build-up of the team.

The importance of thorough pre-commissioning of process plant in achieving a smooth start-up cannot be over-emphasized. Risks associated with short-circuiting these activities to get the unit 'on-stream' include frustrations and sometimes hazards at the ensuing start-up.

Pre-commissioning activities under the direction of the commissioning team must be carefully integrated with the completion of erection through close co-ordination with the site construction manager. Similarly, there must be close liaison with the staff who will be ultimately responsible for operation and maintenance of the plant.

Utilities are generally the first to be commissioned in order to provide facilities such as electric power, cooling water, demineralised water, instrument air, plant air, inert gas, etc (see Chapter 7).

Individual plant systems and equipment items are then checked for completeness against line diagrams, component drawings and schedules while lists are prepared of outstanding items (see Chapter 7).

During systematic checks, commissioning personnel are also on the look out for features which may constitute a hazard to personnel or equipment, for example fire risks from leaking flanges. It is important that the Commissioning Manager's brief is clear in respect of changes to design (see Chapter 3).

Following itemized checks, all vessels are thoroughly cleaned and pipe lines flushed with air or water to ensure that debris is removed. When possible, water flushing operations follow immediately upon hydrostatic and mechanical strength testing of pipework. High pressure steam lines to turbines must be meticulously cleaned by repeated blowing through to atmosphere at high velocity against target plates to achieve the standard of cleanliness required before coupling to the driven equipment; usually this will be carried out in the presence of the turbine vendor's commissioning engineer. Chemical cleaning of boiler systems, compressor connections, etc and any special plant pre-treatment is carried out as necessary.

Catalysts and packings are carefully loaded into vessels using established techniques and applying appropriate tests. Following these operations, air or nitrogen pressure testing up to normal working pressure is carried out to ensure system tightness.

Specialist electrical, mechanical and instrument commissioning personnel are concentrating on their specific tasks throughout this period. Machinery is run off-load and functional testing of instrumentation and control loops carried out after calibration and setting up. Trip systems and other safety devices are carefully checked out in conjunction with process commissioning personnel.

Equipment vendor's commissioning personnel are called forward as appropriate, care being taken with regard to timing and providing adequate notice.

Throughout the pre-commissioning period it is highly desirable that operating and maintenance personnel of the production company or division participate actively in all that goes on. As well as providing an excellent opportunity to familiarize themselves in detail with the equipment procedures, it enables respective team members to get to know their opposite numbers before start-up.

7.   SAFETY

Responsibility for safety should be considered carefully when drawing up contracts and should be defined in the Conditions of Contract. In drawing up contracts for overseas projects, local laws relating to safety and liability for equipment and personnel must be taken into account.

Safety is considered in detail in Chapter 3; aspects of particular relevance are:

• The importance of ensuring that safety considerations are paramount in plant design and operation. Legislation, such as the UK Health & Safety at Work Act, highlights the need for safety audits in plant design and that regard for safety is the responsibility of the individual at all stages of design and operation.

• Safety awareness must not be sacrificed for objectives which may appear to assume greater importance as the commissioning stage approaches. Regular safety checks should be made and attention given to the special precautions required if construction work is to continue in the vicinity of the plant to be commissioned. Escape routes from potentially dangerous areas must be unimpeded and manual trip devices easily accessible in the event of an emergency. Suitable alarmed detectors and escape masks/survival equipment should be available as appropriate when leakage of toxic or other harmful gases, etc may be encountered.

8.   SITE LIAISON AND COMMUNICATION

Misunderstandings and possibly a break-down in communications can arise between the commissioning team and operating staff unless sufficient attention is given to liaison. This is particularly important on overseas projects where day-to-day activities are generally on a more formal basis and often handicapped by language difficulties. Liaison methods should cater for conveying technical advice and response, via interpreters if necessary, and also provision of joint logging of plant operations. When working through interpreters it is good practice, particularly in respect of critical operations, to require that the message be repeated back to the originator before translation.

It is also important to establish lines of communication between day and shift operations. Where a commissioning team is responsible for directing operations it is customary for instructions to be routed through nominated technical personnel of the operating company who in turn supervise their own operators. However, even under these circumstances it is often necessary for the commissioning team to become directly involved in plant/process adjustments. This is most frequent during start-up and emergency situations.

Adequate means of communication between the control room and personnel in field locations should be tried and tested in good time before commissioning begins.

It is also important to maintain adequate liaison with local authorities and the local community in order to ensure good relations.

9.   PERFORMANCE TESTING

Provision for plant performance testing also requires careful liaison between respective personnel of both parties. Broad requirements of such tests will usually have been stipulated in contract documents but it remains for site teams to schedule the test arrangements in detail. These are likely to include selection and calibration of measuring devices, together with application of correction factors and tolerances, sampling and analyses, data-logging and effects of interruptions. It is important that procedures are drawn up and agreed well in advance of proposed test periods (see Chapter 8).

10.   OPERATIONAL TRAINING

On-plant training of operating personnel generally continues throughout start-up and performance testing. One area which usually features prominently at this time concerns actions to be taken on activation of safety trip systems. These will either pre-alarm impending shut down of one or more sections of plant requiring prompt corrective action, or may initiate an immediate trip out. It is very important that operating staff become proficient in dealing with these and other emergency situations. Proficiency requires adequate training, not only during initial instruction but by regular refresher sessions after the commissioning team have completed their involvement.

3. SAFETY

The commissioning period is often the most difficult and potentially hazardous phase in the life of a process plant. As many companies have found, safety related problems during commissioning are often under-estimated. Ways have to be found to minimize these problems.

1. PEOPLE

To achieve safe, effective commissioning, it is advisable to use a technically strong team with relevant experience. Very roughly, the technical staff requirement is about twice that for normal operation. Sometimes it has to be accepted that in order to provide these resources other plants/departments have to release good people for a time to get through this critical period. Experienced contractors can often help either by carrying out the whole operation or by supplementing the Owner's personnel. It is worth remembering that legally companies have to demonstrate that competent staff are employed.

2. SAFETY TRAINING

COMMISSIONING TEAM

The training of the commissioning team (see also Chapter 4) in safety matters is most important. All members of the team should be aware, to an appropriate degree, of the plant design philosophy and the potential hazards, both process and engineering. Where possible, some key commissioning personnel should be involved from the early stages of the project. Part of their remit will be to consider safety aspects of the plant, especially during the start-up and emergency shut-down phases. This knowledge can then be passed to the rest of the team when they assemble.

OPERATING PERSONNEL

The safety training should be comprehensive and must be properly integrated into the total training programme. All personnel should

18

already have had some safety training as part of their induction to process operations, including Permit to Work, Vessel Entry and other formal procedures. Special training on the potential hazards must be given as appropriate. It is useful to involve all grades of personnel in producing the emergency procedures. Shift teams should be encouraged to discuss how they would deal with emergencies which might occur when there are no day management staff to take charge. First-hand practical experience of operating similar processes or equipment is most useful. A model of the plant is also useful, eg, for checking means of escape, locating safety equipment, checking safe access. The commissioning team should review any safety reports (HAZOP, etc) that have been carried out. The team should be made aware of the hazards and types of materials being processed and handled by the plant including all effluent streams.

Special discussions should also take place where appropriate with the factory central safety organisation, the Health and Safety Executive, and with the Local Authorities on how to deal with emergencies such as fire, toxic hazards, etc. Joint exercises can sometimes be organised to try out agreed actions.

In addition to the above, all plant personnel should have regular training in fire drill. It is good practice to issue a pocket card giving the basic actions in the case of fire and other emergencies. Fire and first aid teams should be trained in any special procedures relevant to the new plant or process. They should become familiar with the treatment procedures to be followed after exposure to the chemicals used in the process.

The pre-commissioning period is the ideal time for this training, especially when the team have access to the process plant and can get a feel for the equipment, lay-out, etc. Familiarization helps enormously in hazard avoidance.

3. PLANNING

Planning for safe commissioning is essential; a well planned start-up tends to be a safe one. The degree to which planning is carried out is dependent on the size of plant or nature of the process. In the past, safety matters were often given a low priority and consequently were forgotten or omitted because of more pressing or interesting technical matters. It is vital to ensure that Safety Really Does Come First. A plan should be made of what has to be done when and who will be responsible. It must be understood that safety preparation if not carried out can hold up commissioning.

4.   COMMUNICATIONS

Effective communication is essential for minimizing hazards in process plants. For example:

• Written: The operating, safety, commissioning and other instructions should be carefully written and supplemented by clear diagrams to make sure they are easily understood. They must cover variations in process operating conditions.

• Verbal: Communications between all grades of operating personnel on the plant are most important. Consideration must be given to: 2-way radios, loud hailers, pocket pagers ('bleepers'), internal telephones. Choice depends on local conditions. Effectiveness is more important than cost.

• Visual: Appropriate safety notices, warning signs, etc must be considered (many will be mandatory).

• Audio-Visual: Aids such as films, video tape, tape/slide sequence methods should be considered for communicating important safety messages. Some might be general, eg, dealing with fires, and some might be specific to some part of the process.

Finally, one cannot beat the good old-fashioned dialogue between people, at all levels.

5.   PLANT HANDOVER

Usually the construction team are anxious to get the plant formally handed over for commissioning. It is important that short cuts are not taken in the haste to complete handover.

The primary objective of both the construction and commissioning teams must be to get the plant safely into earliest beneficial operation. It therefore helps to have mutual co-operation so that some of the commissioning team have access to the plant as it is being built. They are able to see the plant grow and therefore have an intimate knowledge which helps towards safe operation later. It is also possible to get many items such as orientation of atmospheric vents, poor access to valves, instruments, etc cheaply rectified before construction is complete when changes would be expensive and time-consuming (but see Chapter 3, Section 8 on modifications). The construction team should give reasonable warning of their intention to offer the plant for mechanical acceptance and preliminary reservation lists, which include safety items, must be drawn up. A typical check list is shown in Appendix 3.1. In this way, many items can be cleared informally. At handover, the plant should be checked line by line, valve by valve, against the 'Approved for Construction' P & I Diagrams to ensure that the plant meets the design intent. The formal handover will usually have a certificate with the final reservation list of remedial work required. It is most important that the plant is handed over in a safe condition, correctly built and to design.

With the advent of big plants and the frequent need to get plants of any size quickly on line, a method of selective handover of plant systems has often been adopted. These are usually utilities, such as cooling water, steam mains, steam raising boilers, etc. Preferably these are treated in separate geographic areas, but this is not always possible. The order of handover is determined by mutual agreement to cover those utility/process areas which are required earlier, or those where because of deliveries etc early completion is easily achieved. Naturally commissioning of a system surrounded by normal construction work is not lightly tackled because of the potential safety hazards involved. Construction personnel accustomed to having relative freedom of working are not usually aware of the hazards or the procedures involved in plant commissioning and so an education stage is needed.

Careful planning and communications are required, at all levels. A clear definition of what is handed over from construction has to be made, eg, with formal marking up of line diagrams, segregation barriers complete with clear signs, clear labelling of pipe every few feet and insertion of clearly labelled slip-plates. Once equipment is formally accepted by the commissioning team, all work must be carried out using full safety procedures eg, using Permit to Work Certificates, Entry Certificates, etc.

6. PLANT PREPARATION

Usually the control room building (not necessarily complete with instrumentation) is one of the earliest areas to be handed over and it is often from this centre that the plant preparation and commissioning work are organised. One of the first tasks before any work starts is to check that all the safety equipment is installed, and the emergency and safety procedures are understood by all concerned.

The next main task consists of cleaning and proving by putting a flow of water or air incrementally through every pipe, valve, fitting, etc at a rate as near as possible to that which will be sustained in actual operation. Where there are non-commissioning team people in the area these operations often have to be carried out at 'safe' times, eg, meal breaks or after day hours. All this preparation progress has to be carefully marked up on master Line Diagrams to check that nothing is missed. Very special attention is paid to ensuring that the lines on each side of relief valves and bursting discs are clear.

After washing or blowing the systems, and carrying out any necessary drying, the plant is usually leak tested by pressurising with compressed air. This is a most important stage from the hazard point of view since the objective is to ensure there are no 'holes' in the system which could lead to leakage of flammable, toxic, corrosive or otherwise noxious material.

At this stage a master Slip-plate ('spades' or 'blinds') Register should be compiled which clearly states where slip-plates are located in the process. The Register must, of course, be kept up-to-date, and signed by the checker.

Very often air has to be purged from a system with an inert gas, eg nitrogen. There should be very strict rules for the admission of inert gas into a plant. Basically, none should be allowed in without the express authority of the Commissioning Manager, who has to be satisfied that all the process equipment has been handed over and therefore entry rules apply to all vessels.

Another important point in the progress of commissioning many plants is that at which flammable materials can be admitted to the system. Again, for the Commissioning Manager to authorize this he must be satisfied that there are no unauthorized sources of ignition. This means, for example, that all burning and welding work must be complete, no blow lamps, tar boilers, etc can be used, and smoking is prohibited. Under very special circumstances, such equipment can be employed in conjunction with a Fire Permit, which is issued after very special conditions and precautions are undertaken. Appropriate precautions must also be taken for other noxious materials.

7.   INITIAL PROCESS COMMISSIONING

Before the final stage of process commissioning of the plant, which is usually the introduction of feed, it is useful to try out as much of the plant as possible with as little risk as possible. For example, some pumps can be run with water if this is mechanically satisfactory. Discrete sections of the plant might be tried with material as near as possible to subsequent operating conditions, shutting them down again, if necessary, when proven. Malfunctions usually develop in the first few hours of operation and it is safer to identify and handle them with concentrated effort, avoiding the temptation to start up too many items of plant at once. Special equipment, eg, compressors, steam boilers, etc, should be started up and shut down by all shift teams to gain experience.

Before process commissioning, the Commissioning Manager should lay down two more safety rules:

• that the plant must be cleaned up to his satisfaction, which usually means that all rubbish, trip hazards, non-essential scaffolding and other materials (especially flammable or toxic) should be cleared away.

• that the person in charge of commissioning a system has personally checked the plant condition to ensure all is safe and correct.

An example of a safety check list before commissioning a plant is given in Appendix 3.2.

8.   MODIFICATIONS

During commissioning the need for plant modifications will arise. These modifications are potentially the greatest hazard to a new plant. Experience, including major incidents, has taught us that all plant modifications must be subject to a strict approval system to ensure that design and safety standards are preserved.

This must include a HAZOP (or equivalent) study to determine the implications for the rest of the plant, eg, insertion of a valve may create a blocking-in or an over-pressure problem. The authorization must be given in writing by a competent person. For larger plants a Commissioning Modifications Engineer who stands apart from the normal pressures of the commissioning team can be appointed. An example of a check list to be used in the safety assessment of a modification is given in the Appendix 3.3.

23

9.   QUALITY ASSURANCE

Where a Quality Assurance system (see Chapter 2) is employed on the project, much of the foregoing should be considered as part of the discipline.

10.   REGULATIONS

For all plants handling potentially toxic or hazardous chemicals, a full assessment of the hazards must be carried out and safe procedures for handling these chemicals demonstrated. This written assessment is required by the Control of Substances Hazardous to Health (COSHH) legislation.

It should be noted that if the process inventory exceeds certain defined limits of flammable or toxic materials, specified in the Control of Industrial Major Accident Hazards Regulations (1984) (CIMAH), then the operation will attract Regulations 6 and 7. This means that for any new industrial activity that qualifies under the regulations a safety case must be submitted to the Health and Safety Executive at least 3 months before the activity commences.

For some processes which involve the discharge of effluents to the environment, discharge authorizations will have to be agreed before process commissioning can commence. For discharges to rivers or the sea an authorization will have to be agreed with the National Rivers Authority under the Control of Pollution Act (COPA).

For discharges to the atmosphere an authorization will have to be agreed with Her Majesty's Inspectorate of Pollution (HMIP). The Ministry of Agriculture Fisheries and Food (MAFF) may also have to be involved in the negotiations. In Scotland the Scottish Office are the responsible ministry. For overseas projects the national regulations regarding the authorization of discharges to the environment must be established and set down in the Conditions of Contract.

11.   POST SCRIPT

One word summarizes the general philosophy of minimizing hazards during process plant commissioning, that word is CHECK and if in doubt RE-CHECK.

4. TRAINING

It is important that all personnel involved in plant commissioning are carefully selected and given planned appropriate training. This will require the transfer or recruitment of people in sufficient time for training to take place. Where possible the organisation chart should be set out early so that teams as they form can learn to work together. Ideally, some senior technical operating and maintenance staff representatives and especially the Commissioning Manager, will have been involved from the initial design stage. They should be experienced people who are then in a good position to oversee the training of the rest of the team.

Training of the total team is usually best organised in appropriate groups, eg, process operations, maintenance (mechanical, electrical, instruments), laboratory.

1.   PROCESS OPERATIONS
Normally the most intensive training is given to the process operating team. The managers and supervisors should be appointed and trained first. Once trained they can in turn participate in the training of the process operators. Supervisors can also be usefully employed in drafting/commenting on operating, emergency, plant preparation and other instructions. Not only does this teach them about the plant but it also increases the sense of purpose and commitment. Training programmes for Supervisors and Operators should contain a large amount of self-learning, eg, by drawing up their own simplified process diagrams, preparing and giving lectures to the rest of the group. The formal part of the training can typically include:
• Induction and Safety: a general introduction to the plant, including the basic safety and site emergency procedures. (See also Chapter 3.)
• Plant Layout: a study of the area in which the particular team will work, locating and identifying all main items of equipment. A plant model is very useful here.

• Detailed Operation: an in-depth study of the operation of the process systems, including familiarisation with appropriate Process and Instrumentation Diagrams, operating instructions, etc.

• Emergency Procedures: failure of power and other key utilities, vital equipment failure, hazardous leaks and other emergencies should be considered. Actions to be taken should be discussed, understood and agreed.

• Isolation for Maintenance: methods for the safe preparation of equipment for maintenance, particular hazards and difficulties should be emphasised.

2.   MAINTENANCE
In general, less formal training will be required for the maintenance as opposed to the process discipline. All personnel should be given the basic safety and emergency procedure instructions as well as an appropriate appreciation of plant operation. More specialist training on new equipment can sometimes be given at the vendor's works, or by special local arrangements off-site. This is particularly important with instrumentation.

Tradesmen require basic safety, emergency and process appreciation training. They should also be given special instructions about the equipment they will have to maintain – especially 'troubleshooting' potential problems.

3.   LABORATORY AND SPECIALISTS
After the basic safety/process appreciation training, personnel should be given training on analytical equipment including sampling methods (especially where new technology is involved). This training should include practice to assure repeatability and accurancy in analysis.

4.   TRAINING METHODS
Once the training needs have been established, the appropriate method can be selected from:

• Custom-built courses, usually 'in-house' and best carried out by the plant technical staff and engineers. Sometimes the company training department will be involved.

• Courses arranged by outside organisations, eg, instrument vendors.

• Training on other similar operating plants.

• Use of training aids, eg, process simulators (often computer controlled) films, videos, etc. Some can be bought as packages, or produced 'in-house'. These can be particularly useful since they can often be available on a 24 hour "self teaching" basis.

5.　TIMING

All too frequently personnel are brought in too late and are inadequately trained before start-up. Senior management should give adequate consideration to proper training of personnel for a safe and efficient start-up. Much will depend on the size and nature of the plant.

Technical staff should be made available as soon as they can be usefully employed, eg, in assisting with the plant design (including overseeing a contractor), participating in Hazard and Operability studies, etc.

Supervisors should be brought in early enough for them to be trained in time to assist in the training of their teams. For large plant, inexperienced operators will probably require at least six months training, including experience on other plants whilst experienced operators may require as little as three months training. The training time for tradesmen can be as little as one month where no new technology is involved, but far longer for specialised equipment.

5. MECHANICAL COMPLETION AND PRE-COMMISSIONING

Mechanical Completion is the term used to cover the phase between equipment installation and the start of process commissioning, in which components of plant are proved to be mechanically fit for their process duty. It can be regarded as a specialized part of the pre-commissioning activity in which each component is prepared for process commissioning, under the control of the commissioning team. A main contractor or equipment supplier is usually responsible for this phase of the work.

In practice the stages of commissioning are rarely so well defined. From the contractual point of view, mechanical completion occurs between "Completion of Construction" and "Acceptance". It may include some specified performance tests and usually refers to individual components of a plant rather than the total plant. This is dealt with in Chapter 2 and Appendix 2.

Since installation may be continuing in some areas of plant while others are being tested and commissioned, site safety must be given detailed consideration; for example, component suppliers and sub-contractors must be carefully controlled during this phase since areas can change classification during the course of construction and commissioning.

Generally pre-commissioning refers to preparing the plant for the introduction of process materials and its main object is to eliminate any problems which might arise at later and more critical stages of plant operation.

1.   MECHANICAL COMPLETION
The sequence of mechanical completion is governed by the overall programme but usually starts with electrical power and utilities.

OBJECTIVES
The objective of mechanical completion is to prove that an installed plant component is suitable for commissioning. This phase includes:

• Checking that equipment is installed correctly: this is usually carried out against checklists that are produced from the component schedules and flowsheets. A typical example is given in Appendix 5.1.
• Proving that the basic components of equipment operate mechanically as specified, or at least acceptably for commissioning.
• Demonstrating that instruments and control equipment work.
• Proving to the commissioning team that equipment items are suitable for pre-commissioning.

ADMINISTRATION
Paperwork is both a tool and a torment in all commissioning. During mechanical completion specialised paperwork relating to units of equipment or components is needed, for technical, safety, contractual and legal purposes.

Specialised requirements are:
• Inspection: This should be carried out before testing is allowed . It must be planned against checklists and may involve specialists (eg, weld inspection). Typical checklists are given in Appendix 5.2.1 and 5.2.2.

Checks are made against the specification and vendors and contractors drawings both for equipment details and system completeness. Systematic recording of checks will be particularly useful where several similar units are supplied . Working drawings are key drawings for system checking, subsequent marking of a "master" set of drawings can simplify recording.

Checks are made of process safety and operability, eg, orientation of relief valves, "fail safe" systems, orientation of non-return valves, access to valves, adequate provision of drains and vents, etc. The plant is also finally checked for cleanliness, removal of construction debris, etc.

Checks are made of physical safety aspects, completeness of safety fittings, handrails, means of access, escape routes, emergency showers and eyebaths, fire extinguishers, etc.
• Testing of equipment items by construction staff: all tests of the component parts should be witnessed.

The object of this stage should be to obtain any completion of erection certificates as set out in the Conditions of Contract, and to ensure that mechanical completion is feasible.

Note: In some cases the warranty period runs from this date, in others from the date of commissioning.

• Paperwork for tests on each plant item, on pipework and instrument systems: Test sheets should be prepared in advance, listing all the tests required together with space for entry and certification of results. Some examples of these pro-formas are given in Appendix 5.3.1 to 5.3.4.

• Paperwork required for handover from the construction team to the commissioning team: To speed up commissioning it is often advantageous for the commissioning team to accept the plant from the construction team in sections, so that plant testing and checking can proceed as soon as possible. The commissioning team accepts full responsibility for any section of the plant after handover. This is when all the documents and certificates of tests already carried out by the construction team or by the original equipment manufacturers must be available.

During this handover period the commissioning team personnel will record their reservations on plant acceptability for correction by the construction team. It is essential that during this period standardised paperwork is used, otherwise misunderstandings can occur. It is important to define the responsibility for accepting satisfactory completion of items on the reservation list.

GENERAL CONSIDERATIONS

• Checks: Before pressure testing, a functional inspection of each system should be carried out to ensure that it has been installed correctly – correct valve types, control valves the right way round, correct instruments fitted, etc. All vulnerable equipment such as pumps and control valves must be fitted with temporary strainers. Instruments should be removed or isolated. The system is then blanked off at each end, filled with water and pumped up to test pressure where it has been designed to be so tested. The line/vessel test pressures must be compatible. Relief valve set pressures should be tested on site and tagged before installation. If necessary relief devices should be blanked during pressure testing of lines.

After the mechanical integrity of each system has been proved, it should be flushed through very thoroughly and drained out. The instrument air supply manifold is normally pneumatically tested. It is essential to blow the air supply pipework through very thoroughly after pressure testing to remove all debris.

• Instrumentation (see Chapter 6): At commissioning, problems are often encountered with the instrumentation. Every effort must be made to ensure that the instruments are functioning accurately and correctly before start up and have not been damaged during commissioning.

• Electrical: All earth continuity must be checked and an acceptable level of resistance to earth of the structure and vessels must be achieved. Wiring must be checked for continuity and insulation resistance. Finally, motors must be checked for correct direction of rotation. Examples of check lists are given in Appendix 5.4.1 and 5.4.2.

• Water Trials: Before running the plant with process materials, it may be necessary to test it out as far as possible by running with water. This also provides the opportunity to give the plant a final thorough flush through. Complete process simulation may not be possible. However, water trials allow the majority of systems to be checked out, and they may allow the plant to be run hot, which may further identify leaking joints. It is essential to make use of the water trials to check the calibration of all the flow measuring instruments.

2.   PRE-COMMISSIONING
The objective of the pre-commissioning phase is to prepare the plant for process commissioning proper. It may involve individual unit operations or a process area containing several pieces of plant.

Apart from the check-list given in Appendix 5.1 the following specific points should be carried out prior to plant commissioning:

• A thorough check of the plant as-built against the relevant plant flowsheets.

• Ensure that the correct maintenance manuals are available.

• Check that the Standard Operating Procedures (SOP's) are available and up to date.

• Carry out simulated runs to ensure that all items of equipment function properly and that the control and instrumentation systems operate correctly (Chapter 6).

• Check that the necessary laboratory facilities are adequate and that the laboratory staff are trained to carry out the required quality checks on raw materials, products, and by-products.

• Ensure that all necessary chemicals and raw-materials are available on site and are of the correct quality and quantity.

• Check that plant operators have been briefed and that they understand the operations of the plant systems.

6. CONTROL SYSTEMS

Whilst it is recognized that there are many plants in existence that do not have computer control systems, many new plants and retrofits do. The emphasis in this chapter, therefore, is on the commissioning of control systems that are computer based. Most of the principles and procedures outlined, nevertheless, are just as applicable to analogue systems as to digital ones.

No attempt has been made to distinguish between different types of system: distributed or integrated, PLC based or otherwise. The guidance in this chapter is essentially generic.

1.   TIME SCALE
The sequential/parallel nature of the various testing and commissioning activities is summarised in Table 6.1 and shown in Figure 6.1.

Note that the testing of the computer control system and the pre-commissioning of the field instrumentation are independent activities. However, it is not feasible to commission them separately because of their functional interdependence.

Much of the instrumentation cannot be installed until after the plant itself is largely installed, and the computer control system is often one of the last items to be delivered to site. Consequently there is an overlap between the installation of the control system and the commissioning of the rest of the plant. This overlap needs careful management to ensure that the integrity of the control system is not prejudiced in the supposed interest of the overall commissioning process.

2.   SYSTEM TESTING AND INSTALLATION
Many computer control systems are purchased on a turnkey basis, in which case most of the testing of both the hardware and the software is carried out in the supplier's works, where the necessary expertise and facilities are readily available. Such testing will be against agreed acceptance criteria and normally results in payment of most of the

system value, the balance being paid on completion of site commissioning.

The testing of applications software by the supplier is usually effected by means of test boxes consisting of switches, lamps, voltmeters, etc. It may alternatively be tested by simulation techniques, an approach which can lead to significant savings in time due to the scope for increased parallel activity. This is discussed fully in Reference 4.

It is important to appreciate that such acceptance testing of turnkey systems is only part, albeit a major part, of the commissioning process which embraces functional checks on the whole system, including field instrumentation, plant interfaces, operator interfaces,

Table 6.1

Activity	Aspects
Field wiring/ instrumentation	Analogue controllers Sensors, transducers, transmitters, actuators. Switches/relays/solenoids/contactors
Computer hardware	Power supply/watchdog Card/rack/frame assemblies Operator stations, Peripherals
Systems software	Communications links Operating system Utilities software/tools Systems diagnostics
Input/Output (i/o)	i/o hardware: Analogue/Discrete/pulse i/o database/engineering units
Configurable software	Database Signal conditioning blocks Alarms/trips/interlocks Analogue/discrete faceplates Overview/trend displays, etc. Alarm lists
Applications software	Sequences Applications diagnostics Mimic diagrams Management information programs

support systems, etc. This chapter concentrates on the post–acceptance, site based phase of commissioning.

Site installation of the computer control system is, in principle, relatively straightforward and is usually carried out by the system supplier. It essentially consists of:

• installing the system cabinets and input/output (i/o) racks in an interface room;

• connecting up the i/o racks to prewired termination cabinets some of which may be in a separate motor control centre, usually by means of multi-channel cables and connectors;

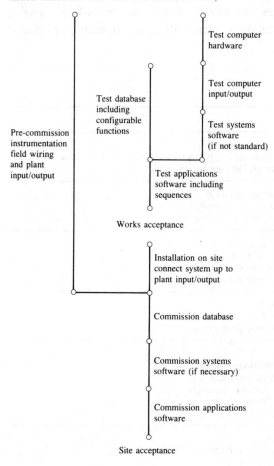

Figure 6.1   Sequence of activities in commissioning a computer control system

- positioning the operator stations and peripherals in the control room and connecting up their serial interfaces;
- powering up the system and carrying out standard system diagnostics routines.

3.   CALIBRATION

Instrumentation is always calibrated by the manufacture but is often recalibrated on arrival at site, especially if there has been obvious damage in transit/storage. When recalibrating remember to:

- calibrate over the whole range and set the bias correctly;
- use the correct static conditions when testing differential devices, eg, dp cells;
- use the correct process medium when calibrating analysers;
- check the local/remote switches function properly;
- ensure that any contacts for initiating alarms are set correctly, etc.

Clearly it is necessary to have access to the various test rigs and equipment required for calibration purposes.

4.   PRE-COMMISSIONING OF FIELD INSTRUMENTATION

Ideally the field instrumentation and process connections, eg, impulse lines for differential pressure (dp) cells, should have been properly installed prior to commissioning as should the infrastructure: power and air supplies, conduits/trunking/cable trays, wiring of termination cabinets, tags, etc. In practice this is rarely so, and the primary objective of the pre-commissioning process is to identify faulty installation.

For detailed guidance on most relevant aspects of process, pneumatic and electrical installation practice, the reader is referred to BS 6739, Reference 5.

The emphasis in pre-commissioning is on checking.

An essential first step in the pre-commissioning of instrumentation is a visual inspection of the installation: its mounting, associated pipework and wiring, to check that the workmanship is of an acceptable standard.

However, the principal check that always needs to be made for each element, *as installed*, is that its calibration, with regard to both range and bias, is consistent with its specification and duty.

Whilst, in general, the major contractor will have overall

responsibility for the pre-commissioning of the instrumentation, there is much to be said, for familiarization purposes, for involving the site instrument maintenance personnel in the pre-commissioning process.

Subsequent checks, to be carried out systematically, throughout the system, include:
- that the primary sensors installed are of the correct type and consistent with their transmitter ranges, eg, orifice plates and dp cells;
- that the process interface is sound, eg, no leaks, impulse lines have correct orientation, right sealing fluids used;
- that the correct pneumatic/electrical interconnections have been made;
- that the grade/quality of all tubing and cabling, single core or multicore, is appropriate to the duty, eg, proximity to sources of heat;
- that all electrical signal and power lines are carried in separate trays, etc;
- that all control and solenoid valves fail-safe and, in the case of control valves, their stroke length is correct;
- that all ancillary devices are properly installed, eg, alarms, limit switches, air filters, positioners, etc.

It should not be necessary to test out every signal and supply line during pre-commissioning. However, in the event of any elements having to be disconnected, maybe because of some other fault that has been found, it is wise to check out the lines when the installation has been restored.

For pneumatic signals and supply lines, instrumentation should be disconnected where necessary to prevent overranging, and the lines flow tested for continuity and pressure tested to approximately 2 bar for leakage. Remember that all air lines must be clean and dry before being brought into service.

For electrical signal channels and power lines, continuity, earthing and screening should be checked. If necessary, compliance with the requirements for maximum loop resistance should be confirmed; likewise the minimum requirements for insulation.

5. CONTROL SYSTEM COMMISSIONING
The principal objective of the commissioning process is to identify faulty installation and/or operation of the hardware and mistakes in the software. Its scope therefore embraces inaccurate calibrations,

incorrectly wired i/o channels, faulty configuration, incomplete operator displays, illogical sequence flow, etc.

The basic strategy for commissioning instrumentation and control systems is the systematic *functional* testing of all the elements and sub-systems against the functional specification.

The elements referred to may be either hardware, eg, transducers, valves, etc, or configurable software functions, eg, alarm lists, display faceplates, control blocks, etc.

The sub-systems will be a mixture of hardware and software, varying in complexity from single i/o channels, interlocks, closed loops and sequences through to complex control schemes and self-diagnostics.

Functional testing of i/o channels entails applying test signals and visually checking the response. For inputs, the test signals are simulated process signals, either generated during water or air tests, or applied manually. For outputs, control signals generated by the computer system are used.

A checklist of some factors to be considered during the functional testing of a control loop is given in Appendix 6.1. A checklist of some factors to be considered during the functional testing of a sequence is given in Appendix 6.2.

In addition to the general purpose control systems, their displays and safety related functions, there are often separate systems dedicated to:

- emergency shut-down (plant protection);
- management information;
- 'packaged' items of plant, eg, compressor sets;
- specialised instrumentation, eg, chromatographs;
- back-up power/air supply.

From a commissioning point of view, they will all consist of similar elements and sub-systems, and the strategy for commissioning them will be the same. However, they often have different functional specifications and particular care needs to be taken at the interfaces between them.

The early installation of the computer control system enables its use as a sophisticated commissioning tool and can potentially have a major impact on the overall commissioning process. However, the impact of this on the schedules for the installation and pre-commissioning of the field instrumentation needs to be carefully planned.

6.   MANAGEMENT

Each of the commissioning activities needs to be broken down into a number of manageable tasks. And for each task a schedule needs to be established with benchmarks for monitoring purposes. Note that the rate of commissioning is measureable, eg, the number of loops/displays or sequence steps tested per day, thereby enabling progress to be reviewed regularly.

For each sub-system successfully tested, the engineer responsible should sign an appropriate test form, preferably accompanied by proof of testing, typically in the form of printout. Examples of various test forms for instrument calibration, alarm system checks, loop tests, etc are given in BS6739, Reference 5, from which the form for loop testing is presented as Appendix 6.3.1.

It is inevitable that there will have been changes to the functional specification necessitating modification of both configurable and procedural software. There will also be mistakes revealed during commissioning. It is therefore necessary to have a procedure to enable software change. Noting the implications regarding safety, this procedure must make authorization of changes difficult, but their subsequent implementation easy. This strategy ensures that software changes are treated just as seriously as modifications to the plant, eg, for Hazard and Operability (HAZOP) purposes, but takes advantage of the user friendliness of modern systems.

The procedure must involve the completion of an appropriate modification control form, eg, Appendix 6.3.2 which outlines not only what change is required, but also *why* it is necessary. The details subsequently become embodied within the documentation.

The position of HAZOP studies in the software cycle is as indicated in Figure 6.6. An important point to appreciate is that it is the documentation, ie the software related parts of the functional specification, which is subject to the HAZOP studies, and not the software itself! And it is against the functional specification that the software is tested and commissioned.

In general, if there has been a change in the functional specification, depending on the nature and scope of the change, it will be necessary to carry out a further HAZOP study before implementing the appropriate software changes. However, mistakes in the software revealed   during   commissioning   can   be   corrected,   without

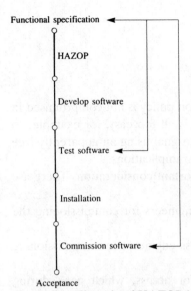

Functional specification

HAZOP

Develop software

Test software

Installation

Commission software

Acceptance

Figure 6.6   The role of HAZOP in software development and commissioning

further HAZOP considerations, provided the functional specification has not been changed.

Some important considerations regarding the modification of safety related software are given in Checklist No. 16A of the HSE Guidelines, Reference 6.

Although implicit in the above, it is nevertheless worth emphasizing that the discs, hard or floppy, and tapes containing the systems software, database and the applications software are themselves covered by the procedure for making software changes. The discs, including back-up discs, should be labelled clearly to indicate which version of software is stored on them. The master should be kept separately and not updated until the software tests have been fully completed.

The segregation policy will have been developed at the design stage. This ensures that the various i/o channels are grouped on the basis of:
- signal type;
- plant item/area;
- process function, etc,
     as determined by the requirements for:
- card/rack organisation;

- intrinsic safety;
- electrical isolation;
- emergency shut down;
- manual operation;
- power amplification.

It is essential that the segregation policy is not compromised in the course of making modifications. It is all too easy, for example, to connect up and configure an additional signal using an apparently free channel and to overlook the segregation implications.

Access to the system is an important consideration. There are two types:

- Access to the software by control engineers for commissioning the system.
- Access through the system by process engineers for commissioning the plant.

To accommodate the needs for access, which peak during commissioning, temporary extra VDU/keyboards may be necessary.

Access needs to be strictly controlled. This is normally accomplished by means of keyswitches and/or passwords, with the levels of access being determined by nature of function/responsibility/ expertise. Passwords and levels need to be recorded and reviewed regularly, with written consent for changes if necessary.

Because of the distance between the various elements of the loops, interface racks, control room, etc. the use of portable phones for two-way communication during testing is essential. This, of course, is subject to intrinsic safety and interference requirements, especially with regard to corruption of computer memory.

7. PERSONNEL

Successful commissioning of instrumentation and control systems needs to be considered within the context of the overall commissioning programme. Good planning, co-ordination, communications, leadership, teamwork and training are all essential.

The commissioning team will need to consist of a mixture of computer and control specialists, instrument and process engineers, the size of the team and its mix obviously depending on the nature and scope of the system. Typical responsibilities are illustrated in Table 6.7.

The applications software is best commissioned by the process engineers who will ultimately have responsibility for operating the plant. In general, it should not be commissioned by the engineers who developed and tested it. Also, it is preferable that the instrument engineers should not be involved in commissioning the applications software; this can lead to software solutions to hardware problems.

It should be stated that the automation function very often becomes the lead discipline upon which the progress of other disciplines depends. It is important therefore to have adequate resourcing at the correct level to handle the inevitable peak demands.

It is normal practice for the system supplier to provide specialist support during site commissioning on a pro-rata basis: it would be contractually difficult to arrange otherwise, there being so many factors beyond the suppliers control that influence the time and cost involved.

There is much to be gained from involving the operators in the commissioning process:

• it familiarizes them with the system and, as such, constitutes training;
• they can contribute to the modifications, eg, mimic diagram layout, warning/alarm settings, etc.

Table 6.7
Responsibilities of specialist disciplines in control system commissioning

	Instrument	Control	Process	Computer
Instrumentation	X			
Field wiring	X			
i/o system	X	X		
Computer h/w	X	X		
Systems s/w		X		X
Database		X	X	
Configurable s/w		X	X	
Procedural s/w		X	X	

8.   DOCUMENTATION

For turnkey systems, once the supplier has been selected, the scope of supply defined and a detailed applications study completed, all aspects of software and hardware functionality should be pulled together into a single document: the functional specification. This becomes the reference source for software development and testing. In particular, it should contain agreed and comprehensive test criteria for all applications software, against which works testing and site commissioning can be carried out, see Figure 6.6.

This process of documentation for software is discussed in detail in the IEE Guidelines, Reference 7. By virtue of this process, applications software may be produced and commissioned in accordance with the quality assurance criteria of BS 5750, Reference 8.

The documentation associated with instrumentation and control systems can be extensive and includes:

- P and I diagrams (Reference 9);
- Loop diagrams;
- Database tables;
- Procedural coding;
- Wiring/circuit diagrams;
- Termination rack layouts;
- Tag number reference lists;
- System Manuals;
- Configuration charts;
- Sequence flow diagrams, etc.

All involved in commissioning have a responsibility to identify any inconsistencies in the documentation and to ensure that they are rectified. It is particularly important that modifications made during commissioning should be incorporated, and it is clearly necessary to have a procedure to ensure that this takes place, see Appendix 6.3.2.

7. PROCESS COMMISSIONING

Process commissioning begins when the pre-commissioning tests have been completed, and faults corrected to the satisfaction of the commissioning manager. It is when plant, equipment, systems or subsystems are put into operation for their normal duty. This is the time when the thoroughness of the planning and preparations described in the previous chapters is put to the final test. It cannot be too strongly emphasized that there are no shortcuts to following those procedures, no matter how large or small, complex or simple the project.

As discrete systems or subsystems become available after completion of the pre-commissioning tests, and faults have been corrected, it is often possible to commission them on process fluid without interfering with outstanding construction or testing work. Because of the potential dangers associated with having some parts of the plant running, while the overall plant is unfinished, the decision to do this should be taken at a senior level. Obviously clear instructions must be given to all construction and commissioning staff to ensure they are aware of the up to date situation. It is good practice for the Commissioning Manager to receive a formal handover certificate from the manager responsible for mechanical completion, verifying completion and listing minor deficiencies.

Where the site or plant is registered to the Quality System BS 5750 (ISO9000) it is important to ensure that the requirements of the Quality Manual are properly carried out as commissioning proceeds; see Chapter 2 (Reference 3).

1.   FINAL CHECKS

Particular emphasis must be placed on safety awareness throughout the commissioning phase as described in Chapter 3.

Before commissioning the plant, it is wise for the commissioning team to run through a final checklist of items which may cause difficulties if not available when required. Such a checklist would include:

- all safety equipment in place and functional eg, safety showers, eyewash bottles, breathing sets, fire extinguishers, etc; emergency procedures known (see Chapter 4) medical/first aid arrangements complete;
- all inspection equipment removed (eg, ladders from vessels) or disconnected;
- test orifices and blanks removed (especially from vents and overflows);
- strainers cleaned and replaced;
- temporary screens to protect pumps and valves in place where necessary;
- liquid seals in vents and manometers at correct levels;
- emergency and normal lighting systems functional;
- rotating equipment guards in place;
- all sources of ignition removed (for plants handling flammable chemicals);
- relief systems fitted;
- access for emergency vehicles is not obstructed;
- tank/vessel bunds clean and empty;
- laboratory prepared to receive samples;
- all documentation available in the plant: calibration charts, log sheets, process manuals and data sheets, handover logs, operator training log, quality manual, etc.

When these checks have been done, the Commissioning Manager usually calls the team of operating staff together to explain the sequence in which he intends to proceed and to allocate specific duties. Communication between individuals and the manager is vitally important during this phase of the project.

2. TYPICAL SEQUENCE OF COMMISSIONING

Depending on whether the plant is on a greenfield site, an extension to an existing complex, or a revamp of an existing plant, a typical sequence of commissioning may be:

UTILITIES:
- electricity, including emergency generators;
- water and its treatment systems;
- compressed air for instruments, process and breathing;

- demineralized water;
- natural gas receiving station;
- firefighting water;
- steam boilers, economisers;
- condensate;
- nitrogen or other inert gas – from cylinders or a production unit.

NOTE: These MUST be regarded as process chemicals and blanked off from process equipment until otherwise authorized.

- refrigeration;
- warm or pressurized water systems;
- drains and effluent treatment systems.

LABORATORY:
Setting up a laboratory is outside the scope of this guide. Suffice it to say that it is a key element which must be thoroughly prepared and ready to deal competently, reliably and accurately with all anticipated samples before attempting to start the plant on process fluid.

STORAGE TANKS/SILOS FOR RAW MATERIALS:
This would also include those required to service utility plants referred to above, eg, fuel and diesel oil, liquid nitrogen or other inert gas, LPG.

ANCILLARY EQUIPMENT:
Many plants have substantial systems which are ancillary to the primary function (eg, reaction) of the plant. Examples are:

- drum melters;
- ventilation and fume extraction systems;
- scrubbers and absorbers;
- pressurised/warm water systems;
- vaporisers;
- vacuum systems including phase separators, distillate receivers and solvent recovery;
- intermediate storage tanks/vessels, etc.

It is often possible to commission these systems progressively as they are completed and pre-commissioned.

REACTION:

The manner in which the plant is commissioned will depend largely on whether it is batch or continuous. Sometimes plants can be divided into several discrete stages where intermediates are made continuously then tested and stored for short periods before proceeding to the next stage. Commissioning of a reaction system is dealt with in more detail in Section 7 of this Chapter.

REACTION MIXTURE WORK-UP:

The majority of plants require further process stages subsequent to reaction. This equipment must be tested and ready to receive reaction mixture as and when it is available from the reactor. Such equipment may include fractionators, evaporators, solvent extractors, crystallisers, neutralisers, filters, blenders, etc. It is sometimes advantageous to commission downstream units by the preparation of a synthetic mix or by importing intermediates from another plant.

PLANTS WITHOUT REACTORS:

Some process plants do not involve reactions so items in the preceding two paragraphs may not apply. In these cases, raw materials may be processed in equipment such as blenders, driers or kilns, pastillators, grinders, granulators, etc.

PRODUCT STORAGE:

This may be for product in various physical forms, ie gas, liquefied gas, paste, slurry, powder, pellets. It may be for intermediate products, recycle streams, by-products or finished product. The time at which they are commissioned and need to be available is determined by the stage of the process they fit into. It is essential, therefore, that the pre-commissioning tests are done to a carefully planned schedule.

3.   QUALITY CONTROL LABORATORY

Before attempting to start the plant, ensure that all the in-process quality checks have been defined, that methods are agreed for various analyses and what corrective action is to be taken if a result is outside the desired range. Equally important is to check that laboratory staff have been trained and are kept advised about when to expect the first sample to be submitted from the plant. If there is serious doubt about any aspect of quality control, it should be cleared up before the plant is started up, in just the same way as if it were a problem with a piece of process equipment.

Key aspects of QC to be checked include:
- hazard potential and treatment data for all material handled;
- specifications, methods of sampling, equipment for sampling, methods of analysis and acceptance tests for raw materials, process intermediates and finished products;
- equipment calibrations;
- all methods of analysis which should have been agreed with supplier, client or customer as appropriate.

A systematic method of recording times and stages of the process from where samples were taken, along with their results, is an essential requirement of the start-up paperwork. Often these results can provide useful clues to solving unexpected problems which might arise, eg, from inaccurate instruments. During commissioning it is inevitable that a larger number of samples will be analysed to check the plant is performing correctly than for routine operation. The laboratory management needs to be aware of this to arrange staffing to suit.

ANCILLARY EQUIPMENT

The process flowsheet must be checked to identify specific pieces of plant equipment which either:
- must be commissioned and operating satisfactorily before feedstocks are introduced to the reactor (for example a scrubber may be essential for cleaning a vent gas before discharge to atmosphere);

or
- can be commissioned on chemicals before starting a reaction proper. An example would be the wash, separation and filtration stages of a plant which is an expansion of an existing process. In this case it may be possible to take from the existing reactor product, which is known to be of good quality, and work it up in the new plant.

It is wise to commission and gain confidence in the operation of ancilliary equipment before starting up a critical stage of the process. This allows effort to be concentrated on the most difficult stage of the process without diversions on trivial faults with ancillary equipment. In the example above, the scrubber could be filled with the specified liquid and the pump run for several days before required by the process. Any leaks or pump seal problems can then be remedied in good time.

Once it is decided which items fall in these two categories, a list of priorities should be drawn up. Where the process involves expensive or hazardous chemicals, consideration should be given to initiating commissioning with relatively cheap chemicals possessing similar properties.

5. STORAGE – RAW MATERIALS

Consideration must be given to availability of raw materials both in drums/packages and bulk. Close liaison with the purchasing department needs to be maintained to ensure that delivery schedules correspond to the commissioning programme.

• Drums: where high melting or high viscosity raw materials need to be heated to charge to the process ensure that drum heating appliances are tested and commissioned well in advance of start-up. It is important to check that temperature controllers and alarms function correctly.

Obvious items such as checking that the correct weight and grade of raw material has been delivered and sampled to check that it meets the purchasing specification can easily be overlooked.

• Packaged dry goods: ensure they are stored under cover and acceptance tested as required.

• Bulk containers: treat as above with additional checks to ensure that the containers are as specified and will connect properly to the plant.

For greenfield sites also ensure that adequate reach and weight capacity fork lift trucks are available to receive and locate the size of containers specified.

• Bulk: raw material storage tanks should usually be commissioned in good time though the cost of storing expensive materials for unnecessarily long periods must be borne in mind.

Potentially hazardous raw material tanks should receive special attention from an experienced commissioning engineer before and during the off-loading of the first tanker. A typical list of items to be checked before discharging into a new tank is given in Appendix 7.

If all the careful testing and preparation has been carried out thoroughly as described so far in this guide then unloading the first consignment should go smoothly and soon become routine. If something does go wrong, the previously thought out emergency procedures will bring the situation quickly under control.

6.   STORAGE – INTERMEDIATES AND FINISHED PRODUCT
Before commissioning the reaction system, it is essential to ensure that any intermediate and finished product tanks have been checked in a similar way as for raw materials – see Appendix 7. Additional items to check are the transfer systems between tanks and road/rail tankers.

7.   REACTION SYSTEM
Only when the Commissioning Manager is fully satisfied that the steps described above have been completed and all equipment commissioned to an acceptable level of reliability, should any attempt be made to commission a reaction system. Because of the wide range of degrees of complexity of reaction systems, they are subdivided into continuous and batch and general guidance is given on typical commissioning procedures for both.

CONTINUOUS PLANTS
These are usually characterized by high throughputs, and fast reactions with relatively low inventories of reactants under closely controlled parameters of flow rates, temperature and pressure. Present day plants generally have some degree of computer or PLC process control. The Commissioning Manager's main concern at start-up is to achieve stable process conditions as quickly as possible and then to be confident of achieving a reasonable running time without breakdown. He will be particularly keen to have confidence in instrument calibrations, software programmes and reliability of prime movers. A typical last minute checklist, additional to that given in Section 1 of this chapter, will include:
• raw material feed tanks at correct temperatures;
• warm-up routines complete where necessary, eg, steam or electric tracing on feed and product lines and process equipment;
• establishing inert atmospheres;
• ancillary systems operating normally;
• cooling water and emergency systems for bringing potentially hazardous reactions under control are immediately operational if required;
• emergency shutdown procedures are clear and understood by operational staff;
• additional support staff are available as required including process

chemists, shift instrument technicians, electricians and specialist fitters.

Once the Commissioning Manager is satisfied that these checks are acceptable he may be able to choose the precise time to start the reaction. Because the hours, days and maybe weeks following start-up are likely to involve intense mental, physical and intellectual strain on the commissioning team he will want to ensure that its members are fresh and alert. There are no hard and fast rules about the best time to start-up; it depends on local circumstances, organization and complexity of the plant. However some points to consider are:

- if starting up on nights or weekends or close to public holidays, are critical equipment service engineers available at short notice?
- avoid starting at shift change and break times;
- availability of key personnel for consultation if needed.

Start-ups naturally attract much interest and concern of senior management. It is important to curb their desire to be present to "see how things are going" during this period of intense activity. One way of doing this is for the Commissioning Manager to give a progress report at agreed times to one nominated senior manager.

The commissioning team will often have to decide whether to continue running a plant in what are normally unacceptable conditions, or whether to shut down to correct a fault. Clearly this will depend on the circumstances but it is only possible to learn the characteristics of a continuous plant whilst it is running. It is often better to keep running to establish that the process is producing the right quality product before shutting down. This reduces repeated start-ups, which generally produce off–specification product, which may be difficult or expensive to recover or blend away.

It is important throughout this commissioning stage to record as much relevant data as possible to check design assumptions and to keep a log of all faults. When the plant is shut down for operational reasons an attempt should be made to correct all known faults.

BATCH PLANTS

These are usually characterized by lower throughputs, slower reactions with relatively large inventories of reactants and multistage reactions or process steps. They may involve multiphase stages, significant changes in physical properties, reaction with or without distillation, etc. Batch plants are often designed to make a wide variety of products. There is a growing trend towards computer control of process parameters and computer or PLC sequence control of individual process steps and alarm handling (Reference 9). Unlike continuous processes batch ones are always transient and rarely have long periods at stable conditions. They therefore require constant attention especially at start-up.

Commissioning a batch plant is generally less demanding from engineering and time pressure aspects, because the processes can usually be subdivided into discrete stages, with quality checks being made between each of them. However, there is greater emphasis on charging accuracy, where concentration effects and contamination can cause undesirable by-products, resulting in loss of yield and increased operating costs. Hence the Commissioning Manager will concentrate on ensuring that correct charges, exact process sequences and critical process parameter controls are achieved on the first batch of each product to be made.

For exothermic batch reactions, the heat release is often controlled within the reactor cooling capacity by limiting the addition rate, or weight added, of one of the reactants. A prime objective of commissioning is to confirm the process design and to establish a reliable, safe operating procedure for routine production.

Batch plants are more flexible than continuous plants and so process conditions and sequences can more easily be altered – both by design and error! A systematic record of process conditions for each batch is essential so that they can be related to quality analysis results. Such changes in process conditions should be formally agreed with the process chemist, and authorized only after a thorough safety/hazard check by the Commissioning Manager.

Batch plant efficiency, or plant utilization, depends on achieving design batch times and batch outputs. This is equivalent to the throughput rate of a continuous plant. It is usual to concentrate initially on establishing that the process and plant are capable of meeting the product specification. Effort then moves towards achieving design yields and batch times consistently.

8.   COMPLETION OF COMMISSIONING
In quality assurance terminology the commissioning stage is not complete until it has been demonstrated to the customer that the plant is "fit for the purpose" for which it was designed. For in-house projects

the customer may be the plant, production or works manager; for large turnkey plants it will be the client company's representative. The "purpose" may be defined in many clauses in the contract; but will generally stipulate a product range of specified quality, yield and production capacity. Hence the customer will require objective evidence that these have been achieved.

For projects where separate commissioning and operating teams are involved a formal handover from the Commissioning Manager to the Operations Manager is essential. The handover must list all items which need continuing technical input to complete any unresolved problems or difficulties and define who is responsible for completing them to the satisfaction of the customer.

For large turnkey projects this is usually provided by guarantee or acceptance runs which are described in the next Chapter.

8. PERFORMANCE AND ACCEPTANCE TESTS

Performance tests are carried out with the plant under design conditions, that is, tested at the design rate and yield using specified-quality raw materials to produce on-specification product.

If the plant or process has been licensed the license will often guarantee the process. Guarantee tests are supervised by the Licensor (or the contractor that engineered the plant) with the plant operated under specified conditions. These conditions are generally outlined in the Contract, but often the actual method of operation and specification of measurement techniques will be arrived at by joint agreement between the Licensor and the operating personnel. If the plant is "own design and engineering", even then an accurate assessment of plant performance at design conditions is required before start-up can be said to be complete.

Ideally the schedule of performance tests should be drawn up well in advance of the actual tests. The duration of tests, performance criteria, conditions governing interruptions, methods of measurement and analysis and allowable tolerances all need to be specified. Methods of determining stock levels at start and finish, recording of instrument readings and sample collection should all be included. Some of these requirements affect the detailed design of the plant and hence must be considered during the plant design stage, eg, provision of adequate flow monitoring devices of the required accuracy.

Performance tests will usually include plant capacity, consumption of raw materials, and quality of finished product. In some instances the tests may also cover reliability, consumption of utilities, and quantity/composition of effluent discharged.

Conditions of Contract for Process Plant (better known as the IChemE Red Book) (Reference 1) states that if the contractor guarantees the performance of the Plant there shall be a Schedule of Performance Tests and that failure of the Plant to pass these tests shall render the contractor liable to pay liquidated damages. Further details of the Conditions of Contract for performance tests are given in that reference.

If these performance conditions are not laid down in the Contract then they should be set by the plant management.

A performance test may be carried out when the conditions presented in the Contract have been attained. These may include:

- the plant operates under steady controlled conditions – ie, all temperatures, pressures, flows, levels and analyses have been fairly constant (or repetitive in the case of a batch process);
- product specifications are being consistently achieved;
- mass and energy balances have been established and show agreement on both a weekly and daily basis.

When all these conditions have been met, the operating conditions for the performance run must be established and maintained for a time period before starting the performance test, or such period may include the performance test. During the performance test, data should be recorded accurately and all pertinent readings verified jointly by representatives of the guarantor and the plant management.

When the data has been collected and processed, corrections will sometimes be necessary to allow for such things as actual cooling water temperature versus design temperature, heat exchanger fouling, etc.

There are three possible outcomes from the performance test:

- the plant achieves the design output and efficiency;
- the plant does not achieve either output or efficiency but the reason can be identified and the problem overcome. Here the contractor may either put the problem right at his expense, or alternatively pay the purchaser an agreed sum so that the problem can be rectified at the next convenient plant shutdown;
- the plant does not achieve either output or efficiency and it is unlikely that it ever will due to design errors. In this case the contractor will have some financial liability and the purchaser will suffer some consequential losses.

9. POST-COMMISSIONING DOCUMENTATION

The changes and modifications to process plant that occur as a result of commissioning experience are the major source of operating hazard.

Pipework may be modified, valve operation totally changed, reactors operated in a manner significantly different from the design concept, and many small changes made to the design as flowsheeted. Sometimes these changes are not properly incorporated in the documentation, so that the risk of misunderstandings during the life of the plant is increased. Temporary modifications are also common during the early operational phases; these bring risks also. These aspects are covered in Chapter 3.

1. MODIFICATIONS
Any modifications that affect standard operating procedures, drawings, plant troubleshooting, plant numbering, equipment schedules and maintenance need to be considered by the commissioning team, and if they have not been covered in the contract are the responsibility of the owner. If serious modifications have occurred a HAZOP or design review study is essential and if necessary expert advice should be taken.

2. RECORDS
All relevant records from performance tests, insurance reports, and first production runs should be incorporated in the documentation system to act as datum points for long term operation.

3. COMPUTER RECORDS
Any computer records, eg control setting changes and other changes to software, must be recorded and if necessary audited (see Chapter 6, Section 6).

4. AUDITS/REVIEWS
A post-commissioning review should be held and information fed back

to commercial departments, designers and contractors. If necessary some aspects should be subjected to independent audit.

During the first few months of operation of new plant the reliability and operability usually improve rapidly. It is important that this experience is fed back to the design staff and where appropriate the equipment suppliers should be advised of shortcomings in their designs.

5.   RESERVATION LISTS

The reservation list concerning defects noted during commissioning should be processed and passed on to operations management. This is essential if rectification must be deferred to a shutdown or otherwise fitted into operating practice.

6.   MAINTENANCE

Commissioning spares should be replaced with the appropriate spares holding and any commissioning oil-fills should be flushed and replaced. Full spares inventory procedures may be needed if the project is large enough. Lists of Service/Maintenance Department addresses and telephone numbers should be made available to operations management.

7.   LOGSHEETS

A developed logsheet and records procedure is an essential component of safe and reliable operation.

10. SPECIAL CASES

1. SMALL PLANT COMMISSIONING

Small plants are affected by all the normal problems associated with major projects such as late drawing office issues, late manufacture, design errors, late deliveries, drawing errors, installation problems, etc. These problems can affect the commissioning activity. The only thing which rarely changes is the completion date. Consequently, the time allocated for commissioning often ends up being half as long as it should be with twice the work content.

On major projects, spread over a comparatively long time scale, there are options to absorb much, if not all, of this slippage. Many contracts however do not fall within this category. A commissioning period of one to six man weeks is often the norm and would be carried out by one multi-skilled engineer.

Because most of these types of plant are to be installed in an existing complex, most of the plant services already exist and have only to be extended to termination points at the new equipment, able to provide the correct rate, pressure and temperature.

The plant will be installed by skilled craftsmen working to plant layout and isometric drawings. The only involvement by a commissioning engineer at this stage, will be a short visit to inspect the installation for familiarization and checking that the drawings are being correctly interpreted. However, he may well have already been involved in a demonstration of the control system at the supplier's premises if it is micro-processor controlled. He will have spent time collating the necessary drawings, line diagrams, data relating to bought-out equipment, process description, contractual documentation and preparing the necessary check sheets which will form the historical data.

The preparation work for contracts of this type is at least as important as the implementation. The job will only be as good as the forethought which has gone into it.

Upon notification that the installation work is complete, the commissioning engineer will move onto site, taking with him the program to load the software and two copies of the program listing. Often it is binding on the purchaser to supply personnel from his engineering department to assist in the commissioning activity. This enables these people to become familiar with the new equipment, to assist in tracing wiring errors and rectification of faulty equipment.

The first activity is to check the complete installation for correctness against line diagrams, orientation of reducing and control valves, familiarization of the whereabouts of emergency stop devices and isolation equipment, and that fail safe devices are normally relaxed the right way.

Next the electricity and air supplies are brought onto the plant, control panel and interface made 'live', micro-processor loaded and validated and item checking commences. Each controlled plant item will have been listed on check sheets by the engineer and each will be checked for drive, feedback and rotation and documented.

Upon completion, water will be introduced to represent product, individual routes set up, either manually or by Operator Entry Code, and the plant hydraulically tested. This will be followed by the introduction of steam and coolant thus enabling conventional instrument or analogue loops to be set up. During this operation, plant operators will have been seconded to the team in order that they may start being trained in the use of the plant.

Finally, still using water to simulate product, the whole plant will be run automatically to ensure that no adverse interactions occur between the various parts of the plant and that functionally it performs to specification. Product trials will follow.

During all these happenings, of course, all the normal protocols regarding site safety and permit to work systems will be observed, but it is to be preferred if special arrangements can be made regarding the documentation associated with these systems. It is not always practical to impose large plant commissioning administration procedures on plant operation being started up by one or two engineers.

Occasional mistakes will be made and the engineer will be expected to correct these as he goes. He may well be also asked to make modifications because the customer has had a change of heart over a particular aspect or, more likely, the operator who will be living with the plant will discover points which, with minor modification, will make his life much easier. He is rarely asked his opinion in the pre-contract stages.

Providing these are minor changes, the commissioning engineer needs no more than verbal agreement from his immediate superior that they should be carried out. What he may not do is to make changes which create a fundamental difference to the plant design philosophy without written authority from Head Office.

To this end, creating and updating 'as left' documentation is one of the most important aspects of commissioning. A daily log of events should always be kept. Such details as Proportional Integral Derivative terms, timer settings, purge times and sterilising temperatures, etc, should be recorded on the appropriate forms, together with a marked up copy of software listing changes and wiring modifications.

The purchaser's personnel should be encouraged to become involved with the project at the earliest possible opportunity, both from an operational and a fault finding point-of-view. That way, when the 'crutch', in the form of the commissioning engineer, is removed, they will not all fall flat on their faces.

2.   DECOMMISSIONING

In projects where an existing plant is being modified, extended or replaced part of commissioning the new plant may involve the closing down and removal of existing plant, or the modification of existing processes.

Features that are particularly associated with this phase of commissioning are:

RECORDS

Records of electrical supplies, drainage routes, vessel contents and structural design may be inaccurate or even non-existent. There is a considerable risk to decommissioning staff and the security of adjacent operating plant during this phase due to error in records.

AREA CLASSIFICATION

The area classification may change while decommissioning is occurring. If plant is to be scrapped the contractor must be carefully supervised for his own safety as well as that of the adjacent plant.

SAFETY

The presence of asbestos, flammable materials, toxic and other hazardous substances may require special consideration in order that the plant can be removed safely and suitable procedures must be devised to cover all aspects.

VENTING AND PURGING

Cleaning out vessels and lines that have been in use usually involves venting, purging and pacifying. These activities must be carefully planned with attention given to pollution and fire-risk. For example, the National Rivers Authority will monitor and agree procedures where river and waterway pollution is possible.

3.   OVERSEAS PROJECTS

Much of the content of this guide is as applicable to overseas projects as to those home-based. However, the former frequently present particular difficulties, and failure to recognise these at the outset can adversely and sometimes seriously affect the success of a project. Some aspects which come within this category are referred to under specific subject headings in the main text. This section seeks to provide a brief summary of some of the more important features affecting commissioning of overseas projects.

One potential difficulty of dealing with some overseas locations is that of protracted timescales. Such a possibility needs to be considered at the bid preparation and contract negotiation stage having regard to commissioning as the final phase of the project and thus likely to be most affected.

Aspects likely to have particular significance in contract conditions and associated terms and conditions relating to commissioning include:

- definition of erection completion and protocol;
- client operator training – 'abroad' and at site;
- numbers of commissioning personnel including specialists; method of payment;
- duties of commissioning team, specialists and other experts. Responsibility for instructions; routing of directions usually via client's technical personnel; recognition that physical operations, etc, are performed by client's personnel under supervision of his technical staff;

- log book/log sheet and operating advice sheet completion; dual/ multi-lingual if appropriate;
- provision of interpreters adequate in number (to include shift duties);
- continuity of services, particularly power supplies and adequacy of emergency supply for essential services;
- provision of laboratory services;
- interruptions to commissioning period;
- effect of local religious observances and similar;
- definition of performance demonstration and guarantee test; interruptions to test runs;
- definition of plant acceptance and protocol;
- provision of office and communications facilities; latter should include availability at times when home-offices/project personnel can be contacted.

A most important corollary of the above relates to the welfare and morale of the commissioning personnel to be deployed and selection of the team itself. Commissioning at an overseas location can put enormous strain on individuals and particularly so on the resident team leader who requires all-round capability in addition to technical competence. Compatibility of the team, particularly under stressful conditions, is also an essential requirement. Terms and conditions for assigned personnel need to take into account such matters as:

- inducements such as monetary incentive and sometimes assignment completion bonus;
- assignment status, (single/married and accompanying children); schooling;
- provision of air fares and excess baggage;
- accommodation and furnishings;
- local currency provision and banking arrangements (if any);
- availability of food supplies;
- local transport including use of vehicles for recreational purposes;
- medical facilities;
- leave frequencies, local and home;
- behaviourial importance, off-duty as well as on-duty;
- compliance with local laws and regulations;
- repatriation arrangements.

It is vital that the commissioning team members are adequately briefed on the project before taking up an overseas assignment;

similarly that they can be assured of prompt response to communications from site since failure to do so can have a very damaging effect upon morale.

Staff assigned should also be familiar with procedures to be followed in the event of national emergencies or other circumstances which might require evacuation of ex-patriate personnel.

4.   BIOPROCESS PLANTS

INTRODUCTION

Processes which utilise mico-organisms to effect conversions and those which further transform materials arising from such biological activity into commercial products have characteristics which set them apart from conventional chemical process operations. Generally metabolic processes occur in dilute aqueous media under mild conditions of temperature, pressure and chemical aggressivity and require small energy levels to promote the catalytic action of enzymes. These process conditions must be carefully controlled in order to maintain cost effective levels of process intensity and conversion efficiency. It is the imposition of such controls (as well as the need to ensure safety, integrity of operation and regulatory approvals) that has most impact on bioprocess plant design and commissioning.

However, before defining the necessary differences from commissioning conventional plant (as set out in the preceding sections of this guide) it is useful to appreciate the range of scale and technology of commercial bioprocess plants. Some biologically based industries such as bread, wine and sewage treatment have pre-historical origins and these remain the largest (volumetrically) process operations with bioreactors of up to 1000 m^3 processing 10,000 m^3 /day of broth. Recent work at laboratory scale with genetically manipulated microbial cells has resulted in microgramme quantities of active therapeutic molecules. For some of these products laboratory scale equipment is sufficiently large to satisfy market demands. The approach to engineering design varies depending on the product. For example, there is little need for sterility, monosepsis and containment at the large end of the scale but almost obsessional care is taken when dealing with active viruses and hormones.

Biological processes tend to be batch operated with various

control conditions that are changed over the course of one to ten days. They utilise natural feedstocks which are also subject to considerable variation. Fermentation broths are complex 3-phase mixtures which although they may have non-Newtonian rheology, must be well agitated for mixing, heat transfer and mass transfer. Often the concentration of biomass and product cannot be directly measured but must be inferred. The product may be biomass itself, an organic molecule which is an excreted secondary metabolite or it may be a complex protein which is accumulated within parts of the microbial cells. Consequently there are many ways by which products are extracted and purified. However, water removal, biomass removal and further separations based on chemical and ionic properties are usually employed to produce a crude product which may be further refined and subjected to chemical conditioning before the final product is realised.

Biological processes are very different from conventional chemical reactions which obey well defined laws of chemistry, reaction, kinetics, thermodynamics and catalysis. In biological processes living cells must be supplied with nutrients and oxygen and as they grow they can be conditioned to effect the required molecular transformations. The approach to bioprocess plant commissioning is in many ways different from the guidelines provided in the preceding sections.

SAFETY

High temperatures and pressures, aggressive reagents and hazards associated with runaway reactions are not generally present on bioprocess plants. The most prevalent physical hazard arises from the inadvertent escape of sterilising steam and simple precautions can effectively reduce such risks.

The real potential hazards relate to process operations involving biologically active materials which may be invasively hostile, infective and cause physiological damage. These hazards are not usually present during the commissioning phase of a project but must be anticipated when, after handover, the operating company introduce live micro-organisms. It is the commissioning and operating engineers' task to ensure that the plant is rendered completely safe for bioprocess operation.

In order to do this, the commissioning and operating engineers have to become involved in projects at an early stage. They need to become conversant with the process technology when the process design is being executed and take part in safety reviews.

Process operator safety, environmental safety and product safety are interrelated and the preparation of documentation that provides the basis to formally establish that safe conditions prevail also includes the preparation of very detailed pre-commissioning, commissioning and operating manuals. The handling of biologically hazardous materials is subject to nationally recognised guidelines and approvals legislation. It is necessary to provide that the design and operation of such plant ensures total containment of viable organisms and potent materials with in-built safeguards to deactivate them before release from the contained process system. It is also necessary to provide documentation concerning the testing of the plant to demonstrate that it operates with a sufficiently high level of reliability and integrity. A complex sequence of tests must be devised to provide adequate evidence of total plant reliability. This comprises systematically challenging process equipment, interconnecting piping systems, utility supplies and control systems to demonstrate that under all possible normal and fault conditions the safety integrity of the plant is not breached.

QUALITY ASSURANCE

In order to comply with legislative requirements a new pharmaceutical facility has to be granted a manufacturing licence before it is permitted to produce a recognised product for which a product licence has been or may be granted. The submission of documentation for approval and the demonstration of satisfactory performance is called validation and this can only be efficiently achieved if this is fully recognised at the initiation of the design, engineering and construction project.

Validation entails the systematic proof by means of witnessed stage-by-stage checkouts, that the process plant, infrastructure and building system meet the approval of the Medicine Inspectorate or other legislative authorities such as the American Food and Drugs Administration (FDA). It is necessary to demonstrate that Systems of Work and Standard Operating Procedures (SOPs) comply with the approved Good Manufacturing Practice (GMP) for the product and that product quality is consistently in compliance with specifications for quality and therapeutic effectiveness. This can only be achieved once a comprehensive quality assurance regime (including engineering records and testing) has been instituted.

The operating engineer is a key member of the project team and he is instrumental in the interpretation of process technology into detailed instructions for plant operations. Because of the special requirements for pharmaceutical plant, it is recommended that at least one engineer is appointed to this task at the start of engineering projects for technical liaison with plant operating company personnel who are normally responsible for seeking statutory approvals. This engineer should also have a special responsibility to provide the preparation of Functional Test Procedures which establish validatory compliance for each equipment item or operating system by bringing together complete design and manufacturing documentation with pre-commissioning test procedures.

Whenever possible, a systems approach should be adopted which provides consistent documentation standards and procedures for every system and includes checklists, summary sheets and referencing guides that interrelate equipment manufacturers data with the relevant stages of validation.

COMMISSIONING ACTIVITIES

Many of the unit operations employed in bioprocess plants have been recently developed from laboratory scale research work and often their pedigree is evident. The commissioning engineer can provide valuable advice concerning design for efficient commercial scale operation if he is involved at an early stage. Unfortunately, there is seldom sufficient time during the course of a project to develop more effective scaled-up process systems and so the commissioning engineer must impose adaptions to operating procedures to account for design imperfections. However, none of the unit operations used in bioprocessing are unique to this industry and whatever scale of operations is required, other non-biological applications of, for instance, chromatographic, ion exchange and ultrafiltration separation systems can be found.

Pre-commissioning bioprocess systems is similar to the normal routines practised in the chemical industry. There then follows a series of special procedures which ensure that effective hygienic and mono-septic operation can be achieved. Complex sequences of washing with surfactants and caustic reagents (or occasionally dilute acid) are followed by rinsing, displacement of air by steam, steam sterilisation and then sterile cooling.

Validated plant is subject to a further series of tests which include challenging the entire process envelope with a simulated external infection and internal process culture in order to prove the integrity and containment.

Utility systems such as Water for Injection (WFI), Clean Steam, Clean-in-Place (CIP) Solutions and Sterile Process Air must be similarly proven. Also the building system itself has to be validated. Many bioprocess operations which contain potentially hazardous materials are operated in closely controlled negative pressure enclosures with filtration of exhaust ventilating air. Sterile and particularly parenteral products are processed in clean rooms which are maintained at positive pressure with filtered incoming air. Validation of building control systems and of personnel changing facilities and Systems of Work are necessary to meet GMP requirements. Manuals for formal test procedures are required to validate these activities.

Very few sensors are specific to the complex compounds present in bioprocesses. Sensors need to be non-intrusive so as not to jeopardize containment or sterility; because of this many process parameters are inferred. Although flow, pressure and temperature can be measured and sterile probes for pH and Dissolved Oxygen Tension (DOT) are used, there is less process information available than is common in chemical plant control systems. This imposes particular problems during commissioning and initial stages of process operation, and much skill is required in the interpretation of operating data. This emphasizes the need for commissioning and operating engineers to have a detailed understanding of process technology and the plant design, and to have been involved in engineering projects from their earliest stages.

Another crucial area in bioprocess plants is the validation of control systems. Instrumentation calibration must be followed by rigorous checking of control system software. Many biotechnology plants are capable of multi-product operation and it is essential to ensure that there is no possibility for commonality in product specific software so that the integrity of GMP for one product does not corrupt a system that has already been validated.

5. SECONDARY PHARMACEUTICAL PLANT

INTRODUCTION

The main differences between the commissioning of a Secondary Pharmaceutical Plant and the commissioning of a Chemical Plant is firstly that the Pharmaceutical Plant has to be very clean, particularly if it is to be used for the manufacture of sterile or aseptic products, and secondly that the standard commissioning phase has added to it a validation procedure.

Bulk pharmaceuticals and generally the active ingredient in a pharmaceutical product, are more than often produced in Primary Pharmaceutical plants which are very similar to Fine Chemical Plants, in that they are capital intensive, are relatively large and work on a three shift system. There is a tendency for pharmaceutical companies to locate their Primary Plants near to their home base. On the other hand, Secondary Pharmaceutical Plants process the ingredients of the product, and fill and pack the medicinal item. These plants are not so capital intensive, work mainly on day shift and employ a higher proportion of females in the work force than Primary Plants.

Pharmaceutical companies have high research and development costs to bear, and in order to provide these funds have to sell their products worldwide, and not just in their home country. Countries often demand that if a pharmaceutical is to be sold in their country, then the company concerned must conduct some manufacture in that country. The result of this is that secondary manufacturing facilities are set up in many overseas countries, with the result that the secondary commissioning activities of large pharmaceutical companies are often done overseas. This is an important factor to bear in mind, as up–to–date knowledge of the construction and operation of pharmaceutical plants with "clean room" facilities is not present in many overseas countries.

COMMISSIONING OF "CLEAN ROOMS"

"Clean Rooms" normally have autoclaves and ovens let into the walls to allow for materials to be sterilised on their way into the room, and to provide for a terminal sterilisation on the way out. There is normally a sequence of two sets of double doors for large equipment to be brought in and out and other doors into staff changing rooms. The floor, walls and ceiling will be of a smooth construction with minimum fittings on the surface, non-porous and easy to clean. The doors could well be of polished stainless steel; air will enter the room from diffusers in the ceiling behind which will be terminal filters, and air will be withdrawn through floor level grids in the walls. Light fittings and windows will be flush fitting on the inside. Services will probably enter by the ceiling above the floor mounted equipment.

Pre-commissioning and the rough cleaning of the room can be done by the contractor or the construction team. Final cleaning should be part of commissioning and be done by the commissioning team and the operating production staff. Before final cleaning, the surfaces must be inspected in detail; if part of the floor is found to be in need of re-grinding later, a complete clean will have to be redone, adding significantly to the commissioning time, so a careful inspection pays off.

When commissioning air handling plant, the main filters are checked for even passage of air which denotes absence of flaws or damage holes. The fault most generally found is where the High Efficiency Particle Arrestor (HEPA) filters do not fit properly into the frames; there is no substitute for strong frames. The shipping and storage of HEPA filters is most critical. Plenty of spare filters should be ordered and the commissioning team would do well to supervise the off-loading of the filters on site and to ensure they are kept in a special store, possibly under the control of the commissioning team. Filter testing equipment is expensive and the testing is a specialist job. It often pays to employ a specialist team to fit and test the filters, even if the team has to be imported from abroad. During the commissioning of the air handling systems, the prefilters, which take the heavy and coarse particles out to prolong the life of the expensive main filters, may become clogged and have to be changed, so the commissoning team must ensure these spares are also available. Terminal filters are fitted onto the end of each duct entering the clean room and these should also be tested.

A suite of clean rooms and changing rooms, laundry, etc, will have planned pressure differentials between them. These differentials have to be set and then the whole system finally checked with the automatic stand-by fans brought in on simulated fan failure while the room pressure differentials are carefully watched to ensure they remain within specification. Controls may have to be adjusted to bring them into line. Fan failure can occur when a door is open, thereby increasing the necessary quick stand-by response. This situation must be able to be handled by the system.

The final cleaning of the room is done with disinfectant prior to a general formaldehyde vapour treatment of the whole ventilation system. Changing rooms and the laundry must be working before the final clean which is done with staff fully garmented. Meanwhile, autoclaves and ovens are commissioned and the floor equipment is wiped down, sited connected to services and covered while final cleaning takes place.

Regular monitoring of the particle count in the room takes place while the air handling system is now continuously running.

For a greenfield site the Quality Control, Analytical Laboratory and Microbiological Laboratory will have to be fully proven before main plant commissioning takes place. The pre-commissioning should be done by the future laboratory staff assisted where necessary by the commissioning team. In an overseas location this calls for early recruitment of staff and their training.

The standard of cleanliness of clean rooms is set down in US and British Standards. BS 5295 calls for a maximum of 3000 particles per cubic metre all below 5 micrometres. US standards are similar but tighter standards are now being introduced and yet tighter standards are in the pipeline. Bugs live on particles so the number of particles is an indication of the approach to sterility. Most of the problems in clean rooms come from people and their clothing, so close attention has to be paid to these factors. People are always shedding skin particles which are generally smaller than the gaps in a woven garment, so the message is to keep the number of staff in a sterile area to the absolute minimum.

After the room and its services are commissioned, the product can be introduced. Thorough checking of the terminally sterilized product is of course essential, but it is even more the case where sterilization would harm the product and that product has to be produced and filled aseptically. Naturally, the points where the product is exposed to the clean room atmosphere have to be specially examined for contamination, and be subject to clean air flow with people activity upstream eliminated, or reduced to a minimum, and nowhere is this aspect more important than in the Microbiological Testing Laboratory.

COMMISSIONING OF GENERAL PHARMACEUTICAL AREAS

Although special precautions have to be taken with products which have to satisfy sterility tests, the bulk of pharmaceutical products, which do not have to meet such stringent criteria, have more and more to meet tough purity conditions. Cross contamination is a hazard in a multi product pharmaceutical factory, and commissioning staff in a new factory are very liable to carry traces of one product to another area on their persons, or more likely on their clothing, if they do not observe strict washing and changing requirements. The performance of the commissioning team in this respect will often set the standard for newly recruited staff in a factory located in an area where pharmaceutical manufacturing behaviour is new. Commissioning staff who are not familiar with modern changing procedures, and the correct wearing of the garments used, should be sent to an established pharmaceutical factory for training. Faulty changing procedures, etc, will result in endless commissioning runs before satisfactory product is made.

All equipment parts which come in contact with product must be inspected by the commissioning team to ensure cleanliness. Failure to do this, and take any remedial cleaning action necessary, will result in more trial runs before satisfactory product results. It is true that the first run of product is a cleaning run, but as will be mentioned later, pharmaceutical products are generally very expensive, and even though rejected product can sometimes be reworked, thorough initial cleaning is cheaper than subsequent product and yield loss, and also saves commissioning time. The commissioning team must not accept the assurance of the pre-commissioning team that everything is adequately clean; it never is.

The commissioning team must pay attention to the testing of filters on the discharge to atmosphere side of air handling and ventilation systems. Inadequacies in this area can result in cross contamination of product areas and products, and in environmental hazards to the public.

VALIDATION

Validation is a procedure designed to ensure that the equipment and procedures of a process will consistently yield a product of the required quality. This proving stage follows commissioning, but in many people's view is part of the commissioning process. Certainly many health authorities will not allow a product to be sold in their countries unless the manufacturing facility has been validated.

Validation generally concentrates on those stages of the process which are vital for a quality product.

Terminal sterilization is such a stage. The validation team, which is often drawn from the future production unit, but can in a new unit be supplemented by selected staff from the commissioning team, will ensure the following:

• The trace or print-out showing the autoclave temperature, time and pressure cycle matches specification, and that research data supports the chosen cycle. That the instruments recording the data have been properly tested, and that testing has been properly recorded. Signed certificates from the Engineering Department will be necessary, as will the production of a planned maintenance procedure, duly authorized, to ensure as far as possible, that verification will continue in the future.

• The steam used in the autoclave, if in contact with the product, must be free of boiler additives and pipe scale. The team will require to see the written results of the steam analysis and the procedure for testing the final filter.

• The team will require to see trial evidence that the sterilization temperature recorded is present throughout the autoclave load. The results of regular monitoring of autoclave temperature across the whole load volume will have to be produced, to ensure there are no cold spots due to inadequate air removal, or due to joint leakage. Samples of final product may have to be taken from various parts of the autoclave and tested for sterility, before the team can be satisfied. The number of samples taken will be far in excess of the number of normal batch samples.

Before validation begins, the engineering and analytical departments have to be fully operational, with written procedures for testing, and testing equipment proven. It can be argued that this should be the situation in any type of process plant, but it is often not the case; in the Pharmaceutical Plant it is essential.

Areas producing sterile products can take up to three months to validate, so validation is a procedure which must be planned into the overall project plan, and steps taken at the design and later stages to arrange matters so that validation can be done as easily and quickly as possible.

THE COST OF COMMISSIONING PHARMACEUTICAL PLANT

When the Board of Directors authorize a project, the decision to invest capital in the venture has been based on the plant profitability. Real profitability depends on the return on the capital spent, when the return is made and how soon production of acceptable product is available at full flow sheet level.

When considering the cost of commissioning pharmaceutical plant, the validation stage must be included. The cost of commissioning is generally between 10% and 20% of the fixed capital project cost, and if the project cost is to represent, as it should, the real and complete cost of moving the project to the stage when acceptable product at full output level is achieved, then commissioning cost in its fullest sense must be included in the initial budget cost. The high cost of the loss of expensive pharmaceutical product, by way of total loss in the initial substandard batches plus the yield losses as the plant is worked up to full flow sheet level, must be included in the original submission to the Board.

Commissioning teams have a responsibility for a much greater share of the project cost and responsibility for providing full production on time than is generally imagined. Planning of the commissioning phases must be done in detail at an early date in the life of the project, as covered in the earlier Chapters.

GLOSSARY OF TERMS

ANALOGUE – Variable signal, proportional to process values.
APPROVED FOR CONSTRUCTION – Engineering drawings and data which carry authorization for use in construction plant or equipment.
ARROW DIAGRAM – Planning diagram which shows by means of arrows the logical sequence of events and inter-dependence of activities.
BAR-LINE – Programme in which activities are charted against time and durations shown by a bar, or line, drawn between scheduled start and finish dates.
BATCH PROCESS – One usually characterized by comparatively slow reactions with relatively large inventories of reactants and multistage reactions or process steps.
BENCHMARK – Common reference point.
BIAS – Adjustment value to allow for error compensation.
BIOMASS – The living micro-organism "product" formed in a biochemical reaction.
BLIND – Blank plate inserted between flanges to effect positive isolation of lines, vessels or equipment.
CALIBRATION – Setting up of instrument to match specific process conditions.
CARD – Assembly of electronic components on a printed circuit board.
CLEAN ROOM – Air conditioned environment with no radiation and an atmosphere essentially dust free.
CLIENT – Organization placing contract for plant, equipment or services.
CODING – Entering software onto a computer.
COMMISSIONING –
i) (specific term)
Putting into operation, or otherwise making 'live', plant, equipment, systems or sections thereof, for normal duty. Adjusting and optimizing operating conditions for attainment of design performance and, where applicable, stipulated guarantees.

ii) (collective term)

Unless otherwise defined, references such as 'commissioning', 'commissioning schedule', 'commissioning team', etc, may be taken to include pre-commissioning and all related aspects of commissioning.

COMMISSIONING MANAGER/CHIEF COMMISSIONING ENGINEER – Person in overall charge of commissioning activities on a specific project.

COMMISSIONING MODIFICATIONS ENGINEER – Person responsible for monitoring and obtaining necessary authorization for all/any modifications to plant and equipment proved necessary during commissioning operations and for ensuring records are properly amended in respect of same.

COMPLETION OF ERECTION – Frequently, attainment of readiness for commissioning of plant, equipment, systems or sections thereof, in which case all pre-commissioning activities are included. In some instances, however, these terms may exclude pre-commissioning, thus denoting completion to the extent of stipulated mechnical tests having been satisfactorily fulfilled; pre-commissioning then follows.

CONFIGURATION CHART – Definition of system software requirements.

CONTACTOR – Motor control relay.

CONTINUOUS PROCESS – One usually characterized by high throughputs and fast reactions with relatively low inventories of reactants under closely controlled operating parameters.

CONTRACTOR – Organization carrying out specified works agreed under contract with Client.

CONTROL LOOP – An instrument loop that has a process control function.

CRAFTS PERSONNEL – Skilled workers specializing in specific technical disciplines.

DATA BASE – Base information

DIGITAL – Two-state presentation of values (eg, on/off).

DISCRETE FACEPLATE – Single display showing loop information.

EARTHING – Bonding of metalwork to low impedance source.

EMERGENCY PROCEDURE – Action necessary to ensure safety of personnel and plant in event of sudden abnormal circumstances.

FIRE PERMIT – Certificate authorizing, under stated circumstances, use of naked flame in areas where ignition sources are normally prohibited.

FRAME – Mechanical mounting arrangement.

GREENFIELD SITE – Proposed location of plant where no other installation already exists.

GROUNDING – Common reference point for electronic signals.

HARDWARE – Electronic components.

HAZOP – (Hazard and Operability Study) Technique for identification of potential hazards and operability problems.

HOME OFFICE – Headquarters office responsible for project and which provides support for site teams.

IBC – Intermediate Bulk Container – A proprietary portable container for the movement of chemicals/powders, etc. (Similar to 'Tote Bin'.)

IN-HOUSE – Work, often relating to a proprietary technology, carried out in owner's design offices.

INPUT/OUTPUT (I/O) – Signals to and from a control system.

I/O HARDWARE – Devices to which I/O are connected.

I/O SOFTWARE – Logic which controls I/O.

INSTRUMENT LOOP – Related elements of a single measurement or control.

INTERLOCK – Logic to prevent maloperation.

LICENSOR – Owner of proprietary technology.

LINE DIAGRAM – Detailing plant and utilities with lines and symbols from which engineering drawings are developed.

LOOP DIAGRAM – Drawing showing all elements of an instrument loop.

LUMP SUM – Usually, selling price for technology, goods and/or services.

MAIN CONTRACTOR – Organization having major responsibility for project under contract with Client; often with responsibility for sub-contractors also.

MASTER LINE DIAGRAMS – Latest revision of line diagrams marked-up to include all changes and modifications.

MECHANICAL ACCEPTANCE/MECHANICAL COMPLETION – see 'Completion of Erection'.

MIMIC DIAGRAM – Portrays plant, process and utility flows in miniature display usually located in control room.

MILESTONES – Agreed objectives for completion of specific phases of the work.

OPERATING SYSTEM – Standard software.

OPERATOR ENTRY CODE – See 'Password'.

OVERRANGING – Driving an instrument outside its normal operating limits.

OWNER – Proprietor; buyer.

PACIFYING – The surface treatment of process pipework and vessels to reduce its surface activity and tendency to react with process chemicals.

PASSWORD – Keyboard sequence required before operator can control actions.

PATHOGEN – An organism or substance which causes disease.

P AND I DIAGRAM – See 'Line Diagram'.

PERMIT TO WORK – Certificate authorizing specific work on plant or equipment in a normally operational area.

PRE-COMMISSIONING – Preparation, functional testing and making ready for commissioning plant, equipment, systems or sections thereof suitably completed and mechanically tested, eg, nitrogen purging; line-vessel cleaning, etc.

PRECEDENCE DIAGRAM – Component of planning method

PERIPHERAL – Auxiliary device connected to a computer (eg, printers' disk drives).

PLC – Programmable Logic Controller.

PROCESS COMMISSIONING – See 'Commissioning'.

PURGING – Displacing potentially hazardous gases or vapour from plant or equipment with inert gas; or sweetening by displacing inert gas with air.

PYROGEN – An agent which if taken into the body produces fever symptoms.

QUALITY ASSURANCE – System which ensures 'Fitness for Purpose' at all stage of project.

RACK – Mounting arrangement for printed circuit boards.

RANGE – Minimum and maximum values.

REIMBURSIBLE CONTRACT – A contract where payment for services performed is at agreed rates and materials, etc supplied are charged for on an agreed basis.

NB: 'Stage payments' may be made at defined intervals of work completion.

RELAY – Electro-mechanical switching device.

RESERVATION LIST – Items against which a qualified acceptance of plant or equipment is given.

RETROFIT – Modification of existing plant usually to an up-dating of design.

RHEOLOGY – The detailed properties of a fluid in motion – usually expressed as the relationship between shear stress and rate of shear.

SENSOR – Measuring device.

SEQUENCE – Succession of logical operations.

SEQUENCE FLOW DIAGRAM – Representation of the interaction of sequences

SERVICE SYSTEM – A system providing an essential service to the process, eg cooling water, power, steam, etc.

SIGNAL CONDITIONING BLOCK – Conversion of a signal from one type to another (eg analogue to digital).

SITE – Location where plant is to be installed.

SLIP PLATE – Similar to 'Blind'.

SOFTWARE – Coding written to instruct a computer system.

APPLICATIONS SOFTWARE – Process plant specific software.

CONFIGURABLE SOFTWARE – Software that can be changed easily by plant operators.

SYSTEMS SOFTWARE – Software that is operating system specific.

SPADE – Similar to 'Blind'.

SYSTEMS DIAGNOSTICS – Facility for fault finding provided by computer.

TAG NUMBER – Unique identification of an instrument loop element.

TESTING – Verifying performance by measurement or operation.

TOTE BIN – A proprietary standard portable container for the movement of chemicals/powders, etc. (Similar to 'IBC'.)

TRANSDUCER – Sensing element.

TURNKEY CONTRACT – A lump-sum price contract covering the entire scope of work, usually from conceptual design to acceptance of the work, including direction of commissioning.

NB: 'Stage payments' may be made at defined intervals of work completion.

USER–FRIENDLY – Operator commands are very simple.

UTILITIES – Services to process plant area such as power, water, air, steam, inert-gas; sometimes referred to as "off-sites".

VALIDATION – Checking.

VDU – Visual display unit.

VENDOR – Seller.

VENTING – Permitting discharge to, or ingress from, atmosphere.

VESSEL ENTRY – Usually a certificate permitting entry to a vessel which might be hazardous in normal use.

WATCHDOG – Automatic check of correct operation of a programmable control system.

WORKS – Factory.

REFERENCES

1. *Model form of conditions of contract for process plants suitable for lump-sum contracts in the United Kingdom* (the *"Red Book"*), IChemE (1981).

2. *Model form of conditions of contract for process plants suitable for reimbursable contracts in the United Kingdom* (the *"Green Book"*), IChemE (1976).

3. *BS 5750: Part 2: 1987 (ISO9002-1987), Guidelines for use by chemical and allied industries*, CIA-BSI (August 1987).

4. Ashley, R., *The installation and commissioning of process plants with fully integrated control systems,* I.Mech.E. Conference, London (November 1984).

5. *BS 6739, Code of practice for instrumentation in process control systems: installation design and practice*, British Standards Institution (1986).

6. *Programmable electronic systems in safety related applications, Parts 1 and 2*, Health and Safety Executive (1987).

7. *Guidelines for the documentation of software in industrial computer systems*, I.E.E. (1985).

8. *BS 5750, Quality systems*, British Standards Institution (1987).

9. Love, J., Strategies for batch control, *The Chemical Engineer*, (September 1987, 29).

APPENDICES

Note: Appendices are numbered in line with the number of the
Chapter in which they are referenced.

APPENDIX 2.1

Defining work and responsibility of construction and commissioning by contractor and the client

PHASE A – CONSTRUCTION AND PRECOMMISSIONING

– prepare plant/equipment for pre-commissioning/mechanical testing

LEGEND: C – Client   H – Contractor   V – Vendor

Work items		Supervised by	Trades & labour by	Inspected by
1. Ensure adequate safety precautions and services available for activities in this and ensuring phases	Phase A-D Phase E-G	H C	H C	C & H C & H
2. Install service gland packing in all minor machinery and drivers		H	H	H
3. Install service gland packing and lubricate all types of valves		H	H	H
4. Check alignment and lubrication of all minor rotating machinery and drivers		H	H	H
5. Fill electrical equipment with oil as required		H	H	H
6. Block-off or isolate all equipment before line flushing and testing		H	H	H
7. Remove bellows-type expansion joints and rupture discs from pipework etc. before line flushing and testing		H	H	H
8. Remove installed relief valves and any instruments liable to damage from lines and vessels if assembly has been made for piping fit-up checks etc. before line flushing and testing		H	H	H
9. Correct any construction errors or omissions		H	H	H

Note: An alternative form of check list can be found in the America Petroleum Institute (API) publication API 700.

APPENDIX 2.2

Defining work and responsibility of construction and commissioning by contractor and the client

PHASE B – CONSTRUCTION AND PRECOMMISSIONING

– prepare services; clean and pressure test systems

LEGEND: C = Client   H = Contractor   V = Vendor

Work items	Supervised by	Trades & labour by	Inspected by
1. Precommission/prepare for duty utility systems and services, inc. package items, as required for testing/pre-commissioning plant systems and equipment	H	H	C & H
2. Check electrical installations for power, lighting, and instrumentation for operability and safety	H	H	C & H
3. Check for correct rotation of minor rotating machinery drivers and carry out uncoupled run	H	H	H
4. Hydraulic and/or pneumatic pressure test equipment to specification requirements to check connections and joints for pressure tightness	H	H	C & H
5. Clean all lines of loose material by flushing, steaming or blowing	H	H	H
6. Hydraulic and/or pneumatic pressure test lines to specification requirements	H	H	C & H
7. Apply any special preparation on inside surfaces of lines as specified	H	H	H
8. Set up relief valves on test rig for witness testing and subsequently re-install in lines	H	H	C & H
9. Install orifice plates after line cleaning and testing	H	H	H
10. Remove all loose material and dirt from inside vessels, volumns and tanks; check/install internals and packings and 'close-up' upon approval of cleanliness and inspection of internals	H	H	C & H
11. After completion of line/equipment pressure testing remove all swing blinds (slip plates) from lines other than those required for operation purposes and install temporary strainers	H	H	H
12. Correction of construction errors and omissions	H	H	H
13. Re-test after corrective work or alteration	H	H	C & H

APPENDIX 2.3

Defining work and responsibility of construction and commissioning by contractor and the client

PHASE C – CONSTRUCTION AND PRECOMMISSIONING

– check and prepare major mechanical equipment, instrumentation, and protection systems

LEGEND: C = Client   H = Contractor   V = Vendor

Work items	Supervised by	Trades & labour by	Inspected by
1. Carry out any chemical cleaning required, e.g. boiler system, compressor suction pipework and lubricating systems, etc.	H & V	H	C H V
2. Check alignment and lubrication of all major drivers, compressors and blowers which have been assembled at site	H & V	H	C H V
3. Clean and flush lubricating oil and seal oil installations and circulate oil in all main drivers, compressors and blowers	H & V	H	H
4. Check for correct rotation of major drivers and carry out uncoupled run	H & V	H	C H V
5. Carry out short running-in tests with air on reciprocating compressors to check bearings, rods, governors, safety devices and ancilliary equipment	H & V	H	C H V
6. Carry out short running-in tests with air (where suitable) on all main centrifugal blowers and compressors to ensure satisfactory mechanical operation when a works test has not been carried out	H & V	H	C H V
7. Carry out short running-in tests on pumps with water (where suitable) to ensure satisfactory operation	H & V	H	C H V
8. Check action of instruments, continuity of thermocouple connections and instrument circuits. Check control valves are correct for direction of flow and action on air failure	H & V	H	C H V
9. Test instruments and loop-check control circuits	H & V	H	C H V
10. Test electrical controls and plant protection systems	H	H	C & H

APPENDIX 2.4

Defining work and responsibility of construction and commissioning by contractor and the client

PHASE D – CONSTRUCTION AND PRECOMMISSIONING
– final preparation for start-up

LEGEND: C = Client   H = Contractor   V = Vendor

Work items	Supervised by	Trades & labour by	Inspected by
1. Check provisions for fire-fighting, safety equipment and communications	H	C	C & H
2. Check that utility systems are fully pre-commissioned	H	C	C & H
3. Calibrate instruments	H & V	H	C & H
4. Check that orifice plates and permanent blinds are installed	H	H	H
5. Charge catalyst(s) in accordance with recommended procedures	H comm	C	C & H
6. Carry out any chemical pretreatment of process vessels required, e.g. gas absorption plant vanadation	H comm	H	C & H
7. Dry out refractory linings other than when included in plant start-up procedures	H	C	H
8. Dry out and purge lines and equipment	H	C	H
9. Test for leak-tightness of plant/systems (standing test)	H	H	C & H
10. Remove, clean and replace temporary strainers	H	C	H
11. Check drainage systems clear and liquid seals filled	H	H	H
12. Check completeness of battery limit connections	H	C	C & H
13. Check battery limits disposal systems are complete and ready for function	C	C	C
14. Check relief systems to flare or blow-down to see no blockages	H	H	H
15. Adjust pipe supports for expansion and loading strains	H	H	H
16. Correct construction errors and repairs	H	H	C & H

APPENDIX 2.5

Defining work and responsibility of construction and commissioning by contractor and the client

PHASE E – COMMISSIONING
– change with Feedstock, etc., start-up plant and operate

LEGEND: C = Client   H = Contractor   V = Vendor

Work items	Supervised by	Trades & labour by	
1. Put utility systems into service in readiness for plant start-up, ensuring that any necessary chemical dosing procedure is established	H	C	
2. Charge feedstock/fuel and other systems fed from outside battery limits, consistent with appropriate safety precautions	H	C	
3. Commence start-up procedures including any necessary refractory dry-out, catalyst conditioning, etc. and proceed to bring plant on-line in accordance with Operating Manual and any supplementary instructions	H	C	
4. Check supports of all hot and cold lines and adjust for expansion strains	H	C	
5. Tighten hot joints	H	C	
6. Optimise operating adjustments; agree procedures for plant performance test(s)	H	C	
7. Maintenance, routine cleaning and normal adjustments to plant	C	C	
8. Complete lagging and painting	H	H	
9. Complete minor construction details	H	H	
10. Record any modifications carried out during commissioning and annotate drawings/diagrams accordingly	H	–	
11. Clean up site	H	H	

APPENDIX 3.1

Reservation check list

PIPELINES AND PIPEWORK

*When carrying out plant reservations checks,
the following list of possible faults should be looked for*

Tick When
Checked

1	Screwed plugs in pipes, only permissible on air, water, nitrogen under 100 psi, 1½″ NB and below	
2	Faulty welding	
3	Correct joints	
4	Odd sized bolts	
5	Black bolts in cold joints	
6	Faulty pipeline supports	
7	Pipe not resting on supports	
8	Are expansion slippers safe? (eg) Will they push off structure when line is hot?	
9	Check spring hanger settings	
10	Faulty spring hangers	
11	Low point drains fitted where necessary, and high point vents	
12	Lagging – missing damaged, loose etc	
13	Vent and drain blanks fitted where necessary	
14	"Weep holes" in Relief Valve exhaust lines, only on Non hydrocarbon or atmosphere RVs	
15	Have all slip plates been removed and spec plates turned?	
16	Spring Hangers – Have restraining pins been removed?	
17	Make sure pipework is up to the P&I diagram specification	
18	Necking off Hazard – is there any equipment, or small bore pipe projection that can be accidentally broken off?	
19	Are small branches, ie drains, sufficiently clear of pipe supports?	
20	Do drain lines run to underground drains? They should not flow over paved areas	
21	Flanges lagged up	

APPENDIX 3.2

"CHEMICALS AND HYDROCARBONS IN" CHECK LIST

Jobs to be done before chemicals or hydrocarbons can be safely brought into the plant	Action	Sign	Date
Complete all necessary reservations			
Nitrogen purge systems prepared and leak tested			
Blowdown system "live"			
Oil/Water separator in commission			
New perimeter fence erected, with "Dematched Area" notices			
Dematching hut in position and gateman available			
Brief all construction people on consequence of plant becoming a "Dematched Area"			
Fire Alarm I/C and all positions tested			
Compressed air sets in position			
Fire extinguishers in position			
Eye wash bottles in position			
Personnel showers in position and checked			
Fire hoses in position			
Fire main I/C and check that hoses fit hydrants			
Drench water sprays tested			
Fire steam hoses in position and check they connect securely			
Fire permits in use			
Flush drains to prove them free from obstructions			
Plant areas clean (fire hazards removed – rags, paper, wood etc)			
Check plant lighting			
Remove contractors buildings, tarpaulins etc			
Remove non-flameproof equipment			
Nominate shift fire teams and arrange practice alarm			
List all possible welding jobs – get most done beforehand			
Check that welding sets pass Works elec. insp.			
Check gas detectors			
Obtain "Means of Escape" certificate			
Check that segregation plates can be easily removed			
Inform Fire Station			
Invite Safety Department to inspect and pass comment			
Carry out thorough search for matches			
Make sure that neighbouring plants know how this affects them			
Inform services (affect their drains)			
Inform Factory Inspector and Alkali Inspector			
Inform local authorities			
Inform Records section			

Final Check by Plant Managers ....

                Date ....

                Time ....

APPENDIX 3.3

Safety assessment

Plant: Title: Reg No.:

Underline those factors which have been changed by the proposal.

Process conditions

temperature
pressure
flow
level
composition
toxicity
flash point
reaction conditions

Operating methods

start-up
routine operation
shutdown
abnormal operation
preparation for
  maintenance
emergency operation
layout and positioning of
  controls & instruments

Engineering methods

trip and alarm testing
maintenance procedures
inspection
portable equipment

Safety equipment

fire fighting and
  detection systems
means of escape
safety equipment for
  personnel

Environmental conditions

liquid effluent
solid effluent
gaseous effluent
noise

**Engineering hardware
and design**

line diagram
wiring diagram
plant layout
design pressure
design temperature
materials of construction
loads on, or strength of:
  foundations
  structures
  vessels
  pipework/supports/
  bellows
temporary or permanent:
  pipework/supports/
  bellows
  valves
  slip-plates
  restriction plates
  filters
instrumentations and
control systems

trips and alarms
static electricity
lightning protection
radioactivity
rate of corrosion
rate of errosion
isolation for maintenance
  mechanical-electrical
fire protection of cables
handrails
ladders
platforms
walkways
tripping hazard
acces for
  operation
  maintenance
  vehicles
  plant
  fire fighting
underground/overhead:
  services
  equipment

Within the categories listed below, does the proposal	Yes or no	Problems and Action recommended	Signed & date
Relief and blowdown			
1 Introduce or alter any potential cause of over/under pressuring (or raising or lowering the temperature in) the system or part of it?			
2 Introduce a risk of creating a vacuum in the system or part of it?			
3 In any way affect equipment already installed for the purpose of preventing or minimising over or under pressure?			
Area classification			
4 Introduce or alter the location of potential leaks of flammable material?			
5 Alter the chemical composition or the physical properties of the process material?			
6 Introduce new or alter existing electrical equipment?			
Safety equipment			
7 Require the provision of additional safety equipment?			
8 Affect existing safety equipment?			
Operation and design			
9 Introduce new or alter existing hardware?			
10 Require consideration of the relevant Codes of Practice and Specifications?			
11 Affect the process or equipment upstream or downstream of the change?			
12 Affect safe access for personnel and equipment, safe places of work and safe layout?			
13 Require revision of equipment inspection frequencies?			
14 Affect any existing trip or alarm system or require additional trip or alarm protection?			
15 Affect the reaction stability or controllability of the process?			
16 Affect existing operating or maintenace procedures or require new procedures?			
17 Alter the composition of, or means of disposal of effluent?			
18 Alter noise level?			

Safety Assessor .... date ....

Checked by .... Plant Manager   Checked by .... Engineer

APPENDIX 5.1

Typical checklist

The IChemE red book (Reference 1) gives a useful aide memoire for mechanical commissioning which is reproduced below:–

1. Installation of gland packing and lubrication of valves and minor machinery, checking rotation of drivers etc.
2. Isolating equipment, removing expansion joints, rupture discs and relief valves from pipework and equipment before line flushing, cleaning and testing.
3. Cleaning of pipework by flushing, steaming, blowing etc.
4. Hydraulic and/or pneumatic pressure testing of equipment and pipework.
5. Application of special treatment or other preparation of inside surfaces.
6. Testing of relief valves.
7. Removing loose material and dirt, installation of internals, inspection and closing up of vessels, etc.
8. Installation of orifice plates after line cleaning, installation of temporary strainers, removal of slip plates, etc.
9. Checking electrical installations.
10. Checking alignment of major machinery and drivers cleaning and flushing lubricating oil installations, etc.
11. Carrying out short running-in tests on machinery as required.
12. Checking action of instruments and control valves, testing electrical controls and alarms, etc.
13. Calibration of instruments.
14. Drying out refractories.
15. Adjustment of pipe supports for expansion.
16. Removal, cleaning and replacement of temporary strainers.
17. Checking orifice plates and permanent blanks, relief systems, safety provisions, etc.
18. Charging catalysts as required.
19. Charging raw materials, process chemicals, fuel, etc. as required.
20. Warming-up, starting-up fluid flows, etc, as required.
21. Tightening of hot joints.
22. Starting-up and operating the various plant items.
23. Routine maintenance, cleaning, plant adjustments, etc.

APPENDIX 5.2.1

Pressure vessels: Inspection

Orientation		
Alignment and level	Vertical	
	Horizontal	
Method of Fixing	Holding down bolts	
	Grouting	
	Davit	
	Agitator Motor/Gearbox/Support	
Nozzles		
Manway		
Handhole		
Vent		
Overflow		
Drain		
Pressure Relief	Valve	
	Bursting Disc	
	Setting labels correct	
Shell mounted instruments fitted per P & I D or ELD	Temperature	
	Flow	
	Pressure	
	Level	
Insulated		
Fire proofed		
Painted		
Vessel identification added		
Electrical lighting	Permanent	
	Emergency	
	Level indicators	
	Viewing	
INTERNAL VISUAL INSPECTION		
Installed and Fixed	Baffles	
	Overflows	
	Weirs	
	Downcomers	
	Trays	
	Chimneys	
	Internal distribution systems	
	Dip Pipes	
	Vortex breakers	
	Packaging support grids	
	Hold down grids	
	Packing	
	Demister	
	Agitator	
	Liner, tiles or protective coating	
Alignment to BS 5276 Part 3 or equivalent and settings to instructions	Tray level tolerance	±
	Weir set height	
	tolerance	±
	Downcomer outlet set height	
	tolerance	±
	Distribution system tolerance	±

APPENDIX 5.2.2

EQUIPMENT CHECK-OUT SCHEDULE PACKED COLUMNS Sheet 1 of 2	Job No: Client: Site:

System/Code No:		VCL No:		
Process Data Sheet:		Design Data Sheet:		
Equipment:		Tag No.		
Carried Out at:		E.L.D. No.		

Check List Items	Initialled as Witnessed:				
	Date	Contr-actor	#	Client	Cert. Authy
Gas inlet/reboiler vapour return deflector(s) fitted & secured as in drwg					
Weir in base of vessel located as in P.D.S. with relation to nozzles					
Liquid baffle(s) vortex breaker fitted					
Gas inlet pipe installed and flow area dimension & location as on P.D.S.					
Demister pad(s) in gas/vapour outlet(s) properly secured					
Liquid inlet distributor installed properly (inc. spray direction) and with flow area dimensions as in drawing					
Liquid distributor tray(s) installed					
Wash trays installed, sealed and secured correctly – satisfactory leakage rate test carried out (trays no. ....)					
Gas redistribution chimney(s) installed properly with flow area dimensions as in drawing					
Draw-off Trays – installed, sealed and secured correctly – satisfactory leakage rate test carried out (trays no. ....)					
Dimensions and number of holes/bubble-caps on wash tray(s) as on P.D.S.					
Weir tray heights as in Process Data Sheet					
Downcomers – width & clearance at bottom lip as in Process Data Sheet					

References:	# = E – Construction
	     O – Commissioning
	     I – Inspection (QC)

THE ABOVE CHECK-OUT WAS COMPLETED TO OUR SATISFACTION:–

FOR CONTRACTOR:		FOR CLIENT:		FOR CERT. AUTHORITY:	
signature	date	signature	date	signature	date

APPENDIX 5.2.2 (Cont'd)

EQUIPMENT CHECK-OUT SCHEDULE PACKED COLUMNS Sheet 2 of 2	Job No: Client: Site:				
System/Code No:	VCL No:				
Process Data Sheet:	Design Data Sheet:				
Equipment:	Tag No.				
Carried Out at:	E.L.D. No.				
	Initialled as Witnessed:				
Check List Items	Date	Contr-actor	#	Client	Cert. Authy
Drain fitted, as in drawing					
Manway in vessel bottom weir installed, secured and sealed correctly					
Baffles correctly positioned in column top, bottom & draw-off section					
Vessel lining as specified in drawing					
Column interior, internals & nozzles clean prior to loading packing					
Packing support grid(s) installed properly & same dimensions as in drawing					
Packing discharge spider fitted					
Packing separated from fines/degreased/pretreated and protected					
Packing installed, as detailed below, hold-down grid(s) installed on bed(s)					
Instruments (inc. pressure/analysis points) correctly located to fulfill requirements of Process Data Sheet					
Check made to ensure proper final joints fitted in vessel flanges					
Flushing & chemical pretreatment carried out					
References:	# = E – Construction O – Commissioning I – Inspection (QC)				

THE ABOVE CHECK-OUT WAS COMPLETED TO OUR SATISFACTION:–					
FOR CONTRACTOR:		FOR CLIENT:		FOR CERT. AUTHORITY:	
signature	date	signature	date	signature	date

APPENDIX 5.3.1

EQUIPMENT CHECK-OUT SCHEDULE	Job No: Client:
CONTROL PANELS	Site:

System/Code No:			VCL No:		

Process Data Sheet: — Design Data Sheet:

Equipment: — Tag No.

Carried Out at: — E.L.D. No.

Check List Items	Initialled as Witnessed:				
	Date	Contr-actor	#	Client	Cert. Authy
Correct materials used, finishing as per spec'n					
Connecting hardware provided as per design					
Piping and wiring devices provided as per design					
Piping at rear of panel secure and of neat appearance					
Wiring at rear of panel secure and of neat appearance					
Tubing and wiring identified by markers					
Annunciator panels comply with design					
Air filters installed and readily accessible					
Instruments located as per design					
Instruments correctly labelled front and rear					
Circuits checked for continuity					
Circuits checked for accuracy of connection					
System isolation tests complete (using 250V DC)					
Pneumatic tubes/connections checked for leaks					
Functional test via simulated field input and output					
Chart drives checked where applicable					
Automatic/manual selection proven where applicable					
Fit of doors/catches/slides checked					
Free of any transit damage					

References:	# = E – Construction O – Commissioning I – Inspection (QC)

THE ABOVE CHECK-OUT WAS COMPLETED TO OUR SATISFACTION:–

FOR CONTRACTOR:		FOR CLIENT:		FOR CERT. AUTHORITY:	
signature	date	signature	date	signature	date

APPENDIX 5.3.2

EQUIPMENT CHECK-OUT SCHEDULE	Job No:
	Client:
ORIFICE PLATES	Site:

System/Code No:		VCL No:
Process Data Sheet:		Design Data Sheet:
Equipment:		Tag No.
Carried Out at:		E.L.D. No.

Check List Items

Initialled as Witnessed:

Tag No.	Orifice Bore		Orifice	Installed	Date	Contractor	#	Client	Cert. Authy
	Design	Ovality	Finish*	Correct*					
		A							
		B							
		A							
		B							
		A							
		B							
		A							
		B							
		A							
		B							
		A							
		B							
		A							
		B							
		A							
		B							

* = Tick when checked

References:

= E – Construction
O – Commissioning
I – Inspection (QC)

THE ABOVE CHECK-OUT WAS COMPLETED TO OUR SATISFACTION:–

FOR CONTRACTOR:		FOR CLIENT:		FOR CERT. AUTHORITY:	
signature	date	signature	date	signature	date

APPENDIX 5.3.3

EQUIPMENT CHECK-OUT SCHEDULE RELIEF VALVES	Job No: Client: Site:

System/Code No:		VCL No:
Process Data Sheet:	Design Data Sheet:	
Equipment:	Tag No.	
Carried Out at:	E.L.D. No.	

Check List Items							Initialled as Witnessed:				
							Date	Contr-actor	#	Client	Cert. Authy
Tag No. R.V.	Design Set (Hot)	Design Set (Cold)	Actual Set	Leak Rate	Blow Down Ring Reset	Exh'st Directn Safe					
NOTE: PRESSURE UNITS USED											

References:	# = E – Construction O – Commissioning I – Inspection (QC)

THE ABOVE CHECK-OUT WAS COMPLETED TO OUR SATISFACTION:–

FOR CONTRACTOR:		FOR CLIENT:		FOR CERT. AUTHORITY:	
signature	date	signature	date	signature	date

APPENDIX 5.3.4

Piping systems test sheet

DESIGN AND TEST DATA		
	Engineering Line Diagram	
	Piping test schedule	
	Piping arrangement drawing	
Availability of the	Pipe, line schedule	
following data relevant	Piping and valve specifications	
to the piping system	Piping isometrics	
	Piping test procedure	
	Piping fabrication and erection codes	
	Pipe support details and schedule	
	Off-site fabricated piping	
	Heat treatment or other	
Test certificates for	Process/Utility valves, control valves etc.	
	N.D.T. (X or Gamma Ray, etc.)	
	In line process equipment	
Piping and valve material analysis certificates		
Welders qualification certificates		
PRE-TEST VISUAL INSPECTION		
Routing and size correct to E.L.D./arrangement drawing/piping isometric		
	Joints bolts nuts and gaskets expansion loops and bellows.	
Installation of piping and piping components complete	Fixed anchors, sliding supports, guides spring or fixed hangers.	
	Jackets/jumpers, tracing, conductive bolts/earthing straps.	
Installation/orientation with respect to flow	Process and utility valves, N.R. and relief valves process control valves orifice plates and flowmeters.	
Location of in line components for access, operation maintenance and safety of operatives		
Location and installation of	Vents, drains, drip legs, drip rings, utility station connections, steam traps, filters, strainers line blinds, spectacle plates, by-passes, instrument tapping points for pressure, temperature and flow, plugs, rodding out points.	
Installation of field mounted instruments i.e. Thermowells, pressure gauges etc.		
Check and ensure system devoid of insulation and paint.		

APPENDIX 5.3.4 (Cont'd)

PRE-TEST PREPARATION	
Prepare a written test plan and mark E.L.D./G.A. with location of all Spools, Spades, Blanks, Vent Valves, Strainers, etc., agree with Site Manager and initiate.	
Obtain Spades, Blanks, Strainers, Vent Valves, Bolts, Nuts, Gaskets and fabricate Pipe Spools.	
Remove R.V.'s for bench testing and Orifice Plates for checking, make good joints or blank off.	
Remove or Spade off any Control Valve or instrument liable to damage under test pressure replace with Spool or make good joint and open any By-pass Valves.	
Spade off or isolate Process Equipment with lower allowable pressure than test pressure.	
Spade off all Overflows, close Drains, fit Vent Valves, ensure test medium available.	
Calibrate Test Gauge and check range adequate for test pressure and detect pressure loss.	
Define testing fluid.	

PRESSURE TEST PROCEDURE		
Site Manager's clearance obtained, other Contractors informed and Safety Notices positioned.		
Ensure all Test Personnel are competent and briefed regarding extent, duration and limits of test.		
Open up system flush or blow through to remove mill scale/rubbish, fit temporary strainers and close.		
Hook up Test Pump to line and test medium, open vents and commence filling system.		
Conduct test per Test Procedure, attend to remedial works and bring to Test Pressure and hold.		
Invite Client's Representative to witness test.		
Prepare Test Certificate and Record.	System Title, Line No's, Plant Ref.	
	No's, Date, Time and Duration of Test	
	Pressure, Test Certificate No. and obtain Client's Signature.	

POST TEST PROCEDURE	
Open up, drain down, remove and account for all Spades, Blanks, Spools, Plugs, Vent Valves, Strainers and Test Equipment flush or blow through and dry out.	
With new Gaskets, re-install all bench tested R.V.'s, Orifice Plates, Control Valves, Thermowells, Flowmeters, Pressure Gauges and remove Safety Notices, etc.	
Check installation complete and purge or chemically clean if part of take-over procedure.	
Complete construction works, e.g. Paint, Insulate, Colour Code, etc.	

APPENDIX 5.4.1

Typical electrical system check-list

1. Examine transformers for mechanical damage, oil leaks etc. Check no-load tap-changer for proper movement.
2. Inspect switchgear for damage and missing parts, alignment, clearance of moving parts, etc.
3. Verify that instrument transformers, instruments, relays, fuses and other devices are of proper type, size and rating.
4. Test or check direct trip breakers.
5. Perform "megger" test (when appropriate).
6. With breaker in test position, test operation with local, remote and manual operation.
7. Test automatic transfer equipment by simulating power failure and under-voltage conditions. Set all relays in accordance with job relay schedule and check operation.
8. Check fuse holders for damage and fuses for size and rating. Witness relay tests and settings.
9. Test cables rated at less than 5000 volts with 500 volt-megohm instrument.
10. Check rotation and ability of motor to synchronise.
11. With motor running, check bearing and winding temperature, rotation and vibration.
12. Check battery and charger for damage and check electrolyte for level and specific gravity. Adjust charging current and voltage.
13. Check emergency generator and automatic starting generation and transfer with simulated loss of normal power.

APPENDIX 5.4.2

EQUIPMENT CHECK-OUT SCHEDULE GENERAL ELECTRICAL INSTALLATION	Job No: Client: Site:

System/Code No:		VCL No:			
Process Data Sheet:		Design Data Sheet:			
Equipment:		Tag No.			
Carried Out at:		E.L.D. No.			

Check List Items	Initialled as Witnessed:				
	Date	Contr-actor	#	Client	Cert. Authy
Cable tray routes as per drawing					
Cable tray supports adequate & secure					
Cable tray assembled & secured correctly					
Cable tay earthing as per spec.					
Cable tray earth continuity checks satisfactory					
Earth cables/bonds securely terminated					
Cable securely banded/saddled					
Cables securely banded/shrouded					
Correct cable glands fitted					
Junction boxes and covers securely fitted					
Flameproof equipment fitted as per spec.					
Lighting fittings correctly erected & secure					
Distribution boards installed and connected as per drawings					
Local control stations installed and connected as per drawings					
All equipment clearly labelled					
Cables & terminations clearly identified					
Area & equipment clear of debris/surplus material					

References:	# = E – Construction O – Commissioning I – Inspection (QC)

THE ABOVE CHECK-OUT WAS COMPLETED TO OUR SATISFACTION:–

FOR CONTRACTOR:		FOR CLIENT:		FOR CERT. AUTHORITY:	
signature	date	signature	date	signature	date

APPENDIX 6.1

Loop check list

Input Channel:

    Check channel no.
Correct tag no?
Correct scaling: range/bias/units?
Test input signal range: top/middle/bottom.
Is signal characterisation necessary?
       eg, square root, linearisation, etc.
Does the input signal need filtering?
If so, check the filter constant is sensible.
Check alarm limits: hihi/hi/lo/lolo.
Check sampling frequency.

Faceplate/bar display:

    In correct overview/group?
Right type of template used?
Correct tag no?
Check info. as per input channel.
Correct eng units shown?
Is set point shown OK?
Is fail safe position of output shown correctly?

Trend display:

    Correct tag no?
Is the time scale appropriate?
Check display frequency.
Are range/bias/units of vertical scale OK?
Correct colour coding?
Does output signal need to be trended?

Archiving:

    Correct tag no?
Correct logging frequency?
How long is data to be archived for?
Check scope/need for data compression.
Are engineering units OK?

Alarm handling:

    Is alarm put into alarm list directly?
Is alarm in right grouping?
Check priority/colour coding is appropriate.
Is alarm logged on printer with date/time stamp?
Do tag no & alarm description correspond?
Can operator override alarm?
Any special requirements for annunciation?
Are standard facilities for acknowledgement OK?
Check any linked trips or interlocks.

APPENDIX 6.1 (Cont'd)

Control functions:

Is set point local or remote?
    If local, is its value set correctly?
    If remote, is its address correct?
Check set point ramp rate.
Is set point tracking required?
Does access to loop status functions need to be inhibited?
Can operator change set point in AUTO?
Can operator change output in MANUAL?
Does loop need to be disabled during start-up?
Are hi/lo alarms on error signal OK?
Has correct control algorithm been selected?
Is proportional action OK regarding oscillation?
Is integral action OK regarding offset?
Is derivative action OK regarding speed of response?
Does loop satisfy other performance criteria?
    eg, stability, noise, etc.
Is the controller action in the correct direction?
Is the controller output bias sensible?
Are there any alarms on the output signal?

Output channel:

Check channel no.
Correct tag no?
Correct scaling: range/bias/units?
Are output channel and controller output consistent?
Check valve opening at maximum and minimum output signals.
Check that valve action is fail safe.
Is there any constraint on the output signal?
    eg, upper limit on valve opening.
Check functioning of any limit switches.
Are time delays for testing change of status sensible?
Check output signal sampling frequency.

Documentation:

Are the loop configuration and P&I diagram consistent?
Is the loop diagram correct?
Are the configuration tables correct?
Is the loop tag no correct throughout?
Is the operators manual complete?
Is the database listing up to date?
Have the discs been updated?

APPENDIX 6.2

Sequence check list

Declarations:

Is sequence no/name correct?
Check variables correctly named:
Integer/flag/block/signal/floating point, etc.
Are variable types correctly defined?
Have constant values been correctly assigned?

Structure:

Are the sequence steps in the right order?
Are the criteria for progression from step to step OK?
Are there any 'never ending' waits/loops?
Check logical for all branching.
Confirm no 'loose ends'.
Are correct subsequences called?
Have subsequences got correct arguments?

Timing:

Are all timing constants sensible/correct?
Check both absolute and lapsed times.
Are there any unnecessary waits/delays?
Have flight times been allowed for?
Sufficient time for discrepancy checking?
Check synchronisation with other sequences.

Contention handling:

Have criteria for handing contentions been specified?
First come first served basis?
Are criteria same throughout the sequence?
Check logic for handling contentions.
Are all relevant signals considered?
Are correct flags set/reset?

Operator access:

Is manual intervention required?
Does operator have full control over sequence?
Check start/stop/hold/restart.
Can sequence be stopped anywhere?
Can the sequence be progressed manually?
Does it have to be restarted from the same step?
Check on need to skip/repeat steps.
Does sequence need to override operator actions?

APPENDIX 6.2 (Cont'd)

Recovery options:

Are correct criteria used for initiating recovery?
Are criteria same throughout sequence?
Check on reserved/released variables.
Are recovery actions correct?
eg, branch forward/back, hold, shutdown etc.
Are actions same throughout sequence?
Branch into separate sequence/subsequence?
If so, branch back to same place?

Recipe handling:

Does the operator assign the recipe to the sequence?
Are the quantities of reagents correct?
Can the operator change the quantities/formulation?
What provision is there for rejecting out of range values?
How are 'as weighed' values handled?
Are the reagents listed in the correct order?
Check the channel no for each reagent feed tank.
Are the operating conditions specified in the recipe OK?
Check set points, ramp rates, time delays, etc.
Are the logical values initialised for the start of a batch?
Check discrete outputs, flags and integer variables.
Have variable alarm limits been defined?

Firmware interface:

Is loop status changed from within sequence?
Confirm output OK if put into MAN.
Confirm setpoint OK if put into AUTO.
Is configuration changed from within sequence?
Check correct blocks/pointers used.
Check correct parameters set up.
Confirm alarm settings OK.
Needs to activate/suspend other sequences?

Sequence display:

Is sequence in correct display group?
Is sequence number/name correct?
Confirm messages fit into reserved area.
Check messages appropriate to steps.
Are operator prompts intelligible?
Is annunciation/acknowledgement of prompts OK?

APPENDIX 6.2 (Cont'd)

Batch logging:

Is standard batch log in use?
Check format appropriate.
What identification is required?
Batch/lot no/sequence recipe.
Is all recipe information included?
What about 'as weighed' values?
Are all actions/events logged?
If not, check that appropriate ones are.
Check provision for logging abnormal conditions.
Recovery options/manual intervention.
Maximum/minimum values of signals.

NB. For sequence terminology, refer to Reference 6.

APPENDIX 6.3.1

Instrument loop check sheet

(Appendix E of BS 6739: 1986, reproduced by permission of BSI)

INSTRUMENT LOOP CHECK SHEET		
Client:	Plant:	
Client's Project No.:	Project No.:	

Loop No. _____ Service _____
Line or equipment No.   Pipe I.D.

Mechanical Checks/Electrical Checks

Measuring element:	Installation correct ☐	Location correct ☐
	Isolating valves correct ☐	Materials correct ☐
	Tapping(s) position correct ☐	Orifice diameter _____
Impulse connections:	Correct to hook-up ☐	Materials correct ☐
	Pressure tested ☐	Test pressure _____
	Steam/elect. traced ☐	Lagged ☐
Field instrument(s):	Installation correct ☐	Air supply correct ☐
	Weather protected ☐	Power supply correct ☐
Panel instrument(s):	Installation correct ☐	Air supply correct ☐
	Scale/chart correct ☐	Power supply correct ☐
Control valves:	Installation & location correct ☐	Size & type correct ☐
	Stroke tested ☐	Positioner checked ☐
	Limit switch(es) set ☐	I./P. transducer checked ☐
Air supplies:	Conns. correct to dwgs. ☐	Blown clear & leak tested ☐
Transmission-pneu:	Lines inspected, blown clear & leak tested ☐	
-elect:	Insulation checked-core to core ☐	Core to earth ☐
	Continuity checked ☐	Loop impedance checked ☐
	Earth bonding checked ☐	Zener barriers correct ☐
Temperature loops:	T/C or R/B checked ☐	Cable to specification ☐
	Continuity checked ☐	Loop impedance checked ☐
General:	Supports correct ☐	Tagging correct ☐

Checked by: Date   Witnessed by: Date

APPENDIX 6.3.1 (Cont'd)

Loop test:

Measurement	Transmitter Input	Transmitter Output	Local Inst. Reading	Panel Inst. Reading	

Control	Controller Output	Transducer Output	Valve Pos'nr Output	Control valve Position	

Remarks:

Checked by:	Date	Witnessed by:	Date:

Accepted by:	for	Date:

Instrument loop No.

APPENDIX 6.3.2

Modification Control Form No:

	System	Loop	Sequence	Display	Trend	Log	Other
Tag/Ref No.							

Description of Problem:

Progression (Initials/Date as approp.):

	Initiated	Authorized	Designed	HAZOP	Checked	Tested	Imple-mented
Plant manager							
Works chemist							
Safety advisor							
Project eng'r							
Process eng'r							
Control eng'r							
Inst. eng'r							

Documentation:

	Operators Manual	P&ID	Loop Diagram	Config'n Chart	Sequence Flow Diag.	Data base Listing	Discs
Page/Diag No							
Updated							
Checked							

APPENDIX 7

Storage tanks – final checks before commissioning

1. Confirm all pre-commissioning checks complete and out-standing items corrected.
2. Confirm all safety devices tested and ready eg. relief valves, flametraps, liquid seals, vents and overflows.
3. Where appropriate bund drain is closed and bund free of debris.
4. Tanker offloading connections, hoses etc. are available and clean.
5. Receiving tank is numbered and labelled in accordance with company standard.
6. Tank and connecting lines are drained and clean.
7. Sampling procedures, analytical method and acceptance criteria have been established.
8. Log sheet is available to record all transfers.
9. Level gauge reads zero.
10. Ancillary equipment has been checked eg. earthing clips, mixer, nitrogen make-up, temperature controller setting, steam pressure to coil, thermometer reading is showing ambient, steam or electric tracing is on to tanker discharge line, remote operation of emergency valves.
11. Safety equipment is in proper location and safety showers work. Material safety data is readily available and Medical Room has treatment information.
12. Containers for collecting sample forerunning and hose drainings are on hand.
13. Equipment and/or material for dealing with spillages is readily available.
14. Operators are familiar with operating procedure, potential hazards and emergency procedure.
15. Confirm delivery quantity, date and time of first tanker.

At the end of the discharge:
1. Check weight received with tanker delivery note.
2. Commission heating/mixing systems as required.
3. Establish inert atmosphere if appropriate.
4. Complete log sheet.
5. Monitor level, temperature, pressure at agreed frequency.
6. Resolve outstanding minor problems.
7. Handover formally to Production.